Weekly Skills Tests
Table of Contents

D1097032

AUTHOR'S INTRODUCTION

Dear Educator:

Teachers have always used a variety of assessment strategies to help them evaluate student progress and to make instructional decisions. Taken together, these strategies can form a coherent assessment system.

A good assessment system has three essential elements. First, it includes a variety of informal and formal assessments. Second, it helps teachers integrate assessment during instruction and use that information to adjust their teaching. Finally, a good assessment system includes both teacher and student self-assessment throughout the learning process. *Houghton Mifflin Reading* provides teachers with assessment options to fill all these needs.

Houghton Mifflin Reading also provides extensive support for assessment integrated into the instructional plan in the *Teacher's Edition* that accompanies the anthology. There you will find informal diagnostic checks and suggestions for reteaching, student self-assessments, comprehension and fluency checks, and test-taking strategies. Other strategies are in the *Teacher's Assessment Handbook*.

Not all teachers, students, or school districts need the same assessment system. By reviewing the various options in *Houghton Mifflin Reading*, you can determine which pieces best meet your needs. Enjoy the many opportunities assessment provides to get to know your students and to help them grow.

Sheila Valencia

FEATURES AT A GLANCE

Weekly Skills Tests

✔ Are criterion referenced.

✔ Test specific skills taught each week.

✔ Include comprehension, information and study skills, structural analysis, vocabulary, spelling, grammar, and writing skills.

✔ Can be administered as individual tests before or after a skill is taught.

✔ Have a multiple-choice format with a single correct answer.

USING THE WEEKLY SKILLS TESTS

PURPOSE AND DESCRIPTION

Purpose

The Weekly Skills Tests assess students' understanding of discrete reading and language skills taught in each theme of *Houghton Mifflin Reading*. The Weekly Skills Tests are designed to help you evaluate students' understanding of these skills and use the results of the evaluation to customize future instruction to meet the needs of your class and of individual students. The tests may also be useful as preparation for certain standardized assessments.

Description

The Weekly Skills Tests are made up of tests covering comprehension, information and study skills, structural analysis, spelling, vocabulary, grammar, and writing skills. Each test includes five multiple-choice questions.

- **Comprehension Skills:** Each comprehension test includes a passage followed by multiple-choice questions that cover key concepts in the text. The test items evaluate students' ability to comprehend the reading and apply the skills to the passage.

- **Information and Study Skills:** This test is designed to assess students' ability to apply the information and study skills taught in the theme. The skills might include one of several special methods of gathering information, such as reading a map, chart, or graph, or using the dictionary.

- **Structural Analysis:** Each test is designed to assess students' ability to apply new phonics and decoding strategies. A test item might consist of a sentence to complete or one with an underlined word or phrase to explain or reword.

- **Spelling:** The spelling test assesses students' ability to recognize the correct spelling of words they have studied in a week. Students read sentences, each containing a blank. They must choose the word that is spelled correctly.

- **Vocabulary:** The vocabulary test assesses students' ability to apply new vocabulary skills. A test item might require students to identify a word that is a member of a particular word family or use a provided dictionary entry to determine the part of speech.

- **Grammar:** The grammar test checks students' understanding of the grammar skills taught in a week.

- **Writing Skills:** The writing skills test assesses students' understanding of the writing skills taught in the theme.

ADMINISTERING THE WEEKLY SKILLS TESTS

You can schedule the use of the Weekly Skills Tests in any of several ways:

- After completing a lesson, you can administer the corresponding Weekly Skills Test to help determine how well students understand the skill taught.

- You can administer selected tests at the beginning of the program or at the beginning of a theme to diagnose students' strengths and weaknesses. You can use these results to plan the appropriate level of instruction.

- You can administer any test during the course of the year in order to evaluate areas where students may need additional help.

When you administer a test, follow these guidelines:

- Check to make sure students understand how to take the test and how to mark their answers. You may wish to administer or review the Practice Test. For the Practice Test, have students read and follow the directions. Then discuss the correct answer with them. You may also want to discuss any questions students have regarding how to mark their answers.

- During the test, allow students to work independently, but help them with any directions they do not understand.

- Allow students sufficient time to complete the test.

USING TEST RESULTS TO PLAN FOR INSTRUCTION

Scoring: Using the Test Record Form

Because the Weekly Skills Tests are a simple multiple-choice evaluation, scoring is direct and objective. Correct answers are shown on the annotated pages of the *Teacher's Edition.*

In general, a score of 80 percent on any test should be accepted as an indication of satisfactory performance. Thus, if a student scores 80 percent or above, you may assume his or her understanding of a skill is adequate.

Tips for Planning Instruction

If a student demonstrates mastery of a skill application by scoring 90 percent or above, consider using the challenge suggestions throughout the *Teacher's Edition* and in the *Challenge Handbook.*

If a student answers fewer than four out of five questions correctly, he or she may need more help with the particular skill. It is important, however, to consider other evidence of a student's growth in reading (from other assessment instruments and your own observations) before concluding that the student is not performing satisfactorily. For example, you may want to review your notes on the observation checklist or the student's work on *Practice Book* pages for the skill. Monitor the student's work on similar skills in the next theme's instruction for an overall view of his or her progress. Check the Skill Finder in the *Teacher's Edition* for the next occurrence of the skill in the level. You may wish to give special attention to the student in teaching this next lesson.

If a student performs very poorly on the Weekly Skills Tests, or seems to not benefit from extra support, she or he may need intervention support. The need for intervention can be assessed using various diagnostic measures, which are outlined for you in the *Teacher's Assessment Handbook.*

For information on how to best accommodate English language learners, consult the *Language Development Resources* book.

HOUGHTON MIFFLIN READING
RESOURCES FOR REACHING ALL LEARNERS

If results from the Weekly Skills Tests determine that a student needs challenge or extra support in a certain skill area, consider modifying instruction using the following resources.

	Extra Support	Challenge
Comprehension	• *Teacher's Edition,* Throughout each selection: Extra Support/Intervention and Previewing the Text boxes; Supporting Comprehension questions; Wrapping Up questions; Review/Maintain Lessons • *Teacher's Edition,* Resources: Reteaching Lessons for Comprehension Skills • Blackline Masters: Leveled Readers; Selection Summary • Other Reading: Theme Paperbacks (below level), Classroom Bookshelf (below level)	• *Teacher's Edition,* Throughout each selection: Challenge boxes and Assignment Cards; Responding questions and activities • *Teacher's Edition,* Resources: Challenge/Extension Activities for Comprehension • Other Reading: Theme Paperbacks (above level), Classroom Bookshelf (above level)
Structural Analysis	• *Teacher's Edition,* Back to School: Phonics/Decoding Lesson in the Strategy Workshop • *Teacher's Edition,* Resources: Reteaching Lessons for Structural Analysis Skills • Intermediate Intervention • CD-ROM: Lexia Quick Phonics Assessment	• CD-ROM: Wacky Web Tales

RESOURCES FOR REACHING ALL LEARNERS (continued)

	Extra Support	Challenge
Spelling	• Basic Words • Extra Support/Intervention box	• Challenge Words • Challenge box
Vocabulary	• *Teacher's Edition*, Extra Support/Intervention box: Vocabulary Support	• *Teacher's Edition*, Vocabulary Skills: Expanding Your Vocabulary • Resources: Challenge/Extension Activities for Vocabulary
Grammar	• *Teacher's Edition*, Resources: Reteaching Lessons for Grammar Skills	• CD-ROM: Wacky Web Tales
Writing Skills	• *Teacher's Edition*, Reading-Writing Workshop: Student Writing Sample; Tips for Getting Started; Tips for Organizing; Writing Traits; Student Self-Assessment • Writing Skills: Writing Traits	• *Teacher's Edition*, Reading-Writing Workshop: Reading as a Writer; Publishing and Evaluating • Resources: Writing Activities • Journal Writing • Revisiting the Text: Genre Lessons; Writer's Craft Lessons

If a student has overall poor test scores but does not seem to be struggling in class, check whether time allotment, directions, or test format may be contributing factors. You may review the Preparing for Testing section in the Theme Assessment Wrap-Up. Also consider the level of support a student is receiving in class. An independent task such as this test may disclose that the student is experiencing more difficulty than may have been apparent. You may want to check in the *Teacher's Assessment Handbook* for other assessment options to help you analyze the student's understanding of the tested skills.

Overall poor performance on tests and in class may indicate that the assigned work is too difficult for the student. In this instance, you may wish to have the student use the Leveled Readers during the next theme.

For more extra support and challenge ideas, consult the *Extra Support Handbook* and the *Challenge Handbook,* as well as the *Education Place* Web site.

Name _____

Practice Test

**Read the paragraph. Then read the question and fill in the
circle next to the best answer.**

Bessie Coleman, who was born in 1893, loved to fly airplanes. Yet she
could not get into a flight school in the United States. In those days, the
schools did not admit people who were African American. Coleman
found a school in France that would accept her. Later, she became the
first African American to earn a pilot's license. When she returned home,
Coleman discovered that the airlines would not hire her as a commercial
pilot. However, Coleman did not give up her dream. She learned how to
do stunt flying, or barnstorming. People who visited air shows loved to
watch her perform. During her life, Coleman also worked to help African
Americans and women who shared her dream.

**Read the following question. Fill in the circle next to the best
answer.**

1. Which sentence best describes what this paragraph is about?
   - ○ **A.** Bessie Coleman overcame many challenges to become a pilot.
   - ○ **B.** Bessie Coleman became a well-known barnstormer.
   - ○ **C.** Bessie Coleman was the first African American to earn a
     pilot's license.
   - ○ **D.** Bessie Coleman went to flight school in France.

Nature's Fury

Level 5, Theme 1: Week 1

Weekly Skills Test Record

Student _____ Date _____

Student Record Form

	Possible Score	Criterion Score	Student Score
A: Sequence of Events	5	4	
B: Information and Study Skills Using Print and Electronic Reference Sources	5	4	
C: Base Words	5	4	
D: Spelling Short Vowels	5	4	
E: Vocabulary Using a Thesaurus	5	4	
F: Grammar Kinds of Sentences	5	4	
G: Grammar Subjects and Predicates	5	4	
TOTAL	35	28	
Total Student Score x 2.86 =			%

Sequence of Events

Read the passage. Then read each question and fill in the circle next to the best answer.

What a Blast!

On a spring morning in 1980, an earthquake shook the ground under Mount St. Helens in Washington. As a result, one side of the mountain slid away.

The earthquake created the largest landslide ever. It also awakened a volcano that had been quiet for over one hundred years. Just after the earthquake occurred, a blast of hot gas, steam, and rock spewed into the air. A huge cloud of ashes rose nearly ten miles into the sky. The ashes were then picked up by the wind and scattered over 35,000 square miles.

Over 150 square miles of forest were flattened by the blast. A scorching fire following the blast burned the forest to the ground. When the fire died down, scientists went in to view the area. They saw that the beautiful mountain scene now looked like the surface of the moon.

A year after the eruption, new plants began to appear at the edge of the blast zone. After several more years, the plants had spread across the area. Later, a few tiny trees sprang up from cracks in rocks. Following the trees, coyotes, foxes, and elk began to return to the mountain.

Today the volcano is a laboratory for scientists, who have made many discoveries. For example, they have learned how an ecosystem can renew itself and about the power of volcanoes.

1. What happened just before the landslide at Mount St. Helens?
   - ○ **A.** Ashes were scattered over 35,000 square miles.
   - ○ **B.** Coyotes, foxes, and elk came to the mountain.
   - ○ **C.** The forest was burned by a scorching fire.
   - ○ **D.** An earthquake happened under the mountain.

2. Which event happened first?
   - ○ **F.** A blast flattened over 150 square miles of forest.
   - ○ **G.** Scientists viewed the area destroyed by the volcano.
   - ○ **H.** A fire burned 150 square miles of forest.
   - ○ **J.** A few tiny trees sprang up from cracks in rocks.

3. When did the events in the fourth paragraph take place?
   - ○ **A.** before the eruption
   - ○ **B.** during the eruption
   - ○ **C.** in the years following the eruption
   - ○ **D.** one hundred years after the eruption

4. Which of these shows the order in which living things returned to the mountain?
   - ○ **F.** animals, plants, trees
   - ○ **G.** plants, trees, animals
   - ○ **H.** trees, animals, plants
   - ○ **J.** plants, animals, trees

5. Which signal word or words from the last paragraph show a time shift from the past to the present?
   - ○ **A.** Today
   - ○ **B.** discoveries
   - ○ **C.** For example
   - ○ **D.** renew

Name _____

Information and Study Skills
Using Print and Electronic Reference Sources

Read each question and fill in the circle next to the best answer.

1. Which reference would you use to find a detailed biography
   of Thomas Jefferson?
   - ○ **A.** atlas
   - ◉ **B.** encyclopedia
   - ○ **C.** thesaurus
   - ○ **D.** dictionary

2. Which reference would you use to look up the pronunciation of the
   word *typhoon?*
   - ○ **F.** atlas
   - ○ **G.** thesaurus
   - ◉ **H.** dictionary
   - ○ **J.** encyclopedia

3. Which reference would you use to find a detailed map of England?
   - ○ **A.** encyclopedia
   - ○ **B.** dictionary
   - ○ **C.** thesaurus
   - ◉ **D.** atlas

4. Which reference would you use to find a synonym for the word *happy*?
   - ◉ **F.** thesaurus
   - ○ **G.** dictionary
   - ○ **H.** encyclopedia
   - ○ **J.** atlas

5. In which reference might you find a list of some poems written
   by Robert Frost?
   - ◉ **A.** encyclopedia
   - ○ **B.** dictionary
   - ○ **C.** thesaurus
   - ○ **D.** atlas

Base Words

Choose the correct base word for each underlined word below.
Fill in the circle next to the best answer.

1. The wind blew for hours without <u>stopping</u>.
   - ○ **A.** stopp
   - ○ **B.** stops
   - ◉ **C.** stop
   - ○ **D.** stopped

2. Reporters <u>questioned</u> the people who saw the volcano erupt.
   - ○ **F.** quest
   - ○ **G.** questione
   - ○ **H.** questioning
   - ◉ **J.** question

3. These storm winds were <u>stronger</u> than those of last year.
   - ◉ **A.** strong
   - ○ **B.** stron
   - ○ **C.** stronge
   - ○ **D.** strongest

4. He <u>watched</u> in horror as the water rose.
   - ◉ **F.** watch
   - ○ **G.** watcher
   - ○ **H.** watches
   - ○ **J.** watching

5. A waterspout is a tornado that <u>travels</u> over water.
   - ○ **A.** traveled
   - ◉ **B.** travel
   - ○ **C.** trav
   - ○ **D.** traveling

STOP

Name _____

Spelling Short Vowels

Find the correctly spelled word to complete each sentence.
Fill in the circle beside your answer.

1. The _____ current carried the small raft.

    ○ **A.** sewift   ◉ **C.** swift
    ○ **B.** sweft   ○ **D.** swieft

2. I had never _____ in a tent before.

    ○ **F.** sleept   ◉ **H.** slept
    ○ **G.** sleapt   ○ **J.** slepth

3. Tonight we plan to sleep in _____ beds.

    ○ **A.** bounk   ◉ **C.** bunk
    ○ **B.** bunck   ○ **D.** buunk

4. The _____ earth makes it difficult to sleep in a sleeping bag on the ground.

    ○ **F.** daimp   ○ **H.** deamp
    ○ **G.** demp   ◉ **J.** damp

5. We paddled our canoe over to the _____.

    ◉ **A.** dock   ○ **C.** dahk
    ○ **B.** dawk   ○ **D.** dook

STOP

Vocabulary Using a Thesaurus

Choose the word that can best replace the underlined word in each sentence. Fill in the circle next to the best answer.

1. Photographing storms is a very <u>risky</u> job.

- ○ **A.** uncertain
- ○ **B.** reliable
- ○ **C.** false
- ◉ **D.** dangerous

2. The copilot helped to <u>steer</u> the airplane during the storm.

- ○ **F.** review
- ◉ **G.** guide
- ○ **H.** surround
- ○ **J.** invade

3. My mother is an <u>expert</u> on tropical storms.

- ○ **A.** speaker
- ○ **B.** official
- ○ **C.** teacher
- ◉ **D.** authority

4. Who can <u>predict</u> the weather?

- ◉ **F.** foretell
- ○ **G.** change
- ○ **H.** ignore
- ○ **J.** explain

5. We heard the tornado <u>alert</u> on the truck radio.

- ○ **A.** program
- ○ **B.** answer
- ◉ **C.** warning
- ○ **D.** subject

Grammar Kinds of Sentences

Read the directions. Then fill in the circle next to the best answer.

1. Choose the exclamatory sentence.
    - ○ **A.** My sister was once in a hurricane.
    - ○ **B.** She was visiting our aunt in North Carolina.
    - ○ **C.** She saw a tree blow over!
    - ○ **D.** Have you ever been in such a storm?

2. Choose the interrogative sentence.
    - ○ **F.** Do you know why hurricanes have names?
    - ○ **G.** Naming them helps scientists keep track of the storms.
    - ○ **H.** There once was a hurricane named Betsy.
    - ○ **J.** That's my mother's name!

3. Choose the imperative sentence.
    - ○ **A.** Did you hear about the storm last night?
    - ○ **B.** It rained over two inches in one hour.
    - ○ **C.** The wind blew our newspaper down the street.
    - ○ **D.** Find the newspaper and bring it back.

4. Choose the declarative sentence.
    - ○ **F.** Why can't Grandma come to visit on Saturday?
    - ○ **G.** She has to clean up after the storm.
    - ○ **H.** Please go patch the roof.
    - ○ **J.** That will take two days!

5. Choose the imperative sentence.
    - ○ **A.** Did you watch the television footage about the huge storm last night?
    - ○ **B.** It was near New Orleans in Louisiana.
    - ○ **C.** What an incredible storm it was!
    - ○ **D.** Watch the footage on television tonight.

Name _____

Grammar Subjects and Predicates

Read the directions. Then fill in the circle next to the best answer.

1. Choose the complete subject in the following sentence:

The powerful hurricane in Florida caused great destruction.

   ○ **A.** The powerful hurricane in Florida
   ○ **B.** hurricane
   ○ **C.** The powerful hurricane
   ○ **D.** caused great destruction.

2. Choose the complete predicate in the following sentence:

The huge tornado destroyed everything in its path.

   ○ **F.** The huge tornado
   ○ **G.** destroyed everything
   ○ **H.** tornado
   ○ **J.** destroyed everything in its path.

3. Choose the simple predicate in the following sentence:

The beautiful Mount Fuji last erupted in 1707.

   ○ **A.** Mount Fuji last erupted
   ○ **B.** erupted
   ○ **C.** The beautiful Mount Fuji
   ○ **D.** erupted in 1707.

4. Choose the simple subject in the following sentence:

The monsoon in India flooded many homes and buildings.

- ○ **F.** The monsoon in India
- ◉ **G.** monsoon
- ○ **H.** flooded
- ○ **J.** flooded many homes and buildings.

5. Choose the complete predicate in the following sentence:

A large bolt of lightning struck the empty warehouse.

- ○ **A.** A large bolt of lightning
- ○ **B.** bolt
- ○ **C.** struck
- ◉ **D.** struck the empty warehouse.

Nature's Fury

Level 5, Theme 1: Week 2

Weekly Skills Test Record

Student _____ Date _____

Student Record Form	Possible Score	Criterion Score	Student Score
A: Text Organization	5	4	
B: Syllabication	5	4	
C: Spelling Spell Long *a*, Long *e*, and Long *i*	5	4	
D: Vocabulary Dictionary: Guide Words	5	4	
E: Grammar Conjunctions	5	4	
F: Grammar Compound Sentences	5	4	
G: Writing Skills Capitalizing and Punctuating Sentences	5	4	
TOTAL	35	28	
Total Student Score x 2.86 =			%

Name _____

Text Organization

Read the passage. Then read each question and fill in the circle next to the best answer.

Spotting a Tornado

A small funnel-shaped cloud dropped from the slowly moving storm. As it grew larger, the cloud twisted violently like an angry snake. Two miles away, the people in the small town of Water Valley, Ohio, watched in horror.

The people of Water Valley had reason to be frightened. Small funnel clouds can quickly turn into fierce tornadoes that touch the ground. The wind speeds in a tornado may reach 200 to 300 miles per hour. Such powerful tornadoes can destroy everything in their path.

Tornadoes are carried along by the storm clouds in which they form. They may move in a straight path or appear to skip from place to place. This irregular movement makes it difficult to guess where tornadoes will move next — and it makes them more dangerous.

Look at the pictures below. If you ever see such a sight, take cover.

A tornado first appears as a small funnel-shaped cloud dropping out of storm clouds.

Go on

1. How is the passage organized?

 ◯ **A.** by listing the events in the Water Valley, Ohio, tornado
 ◯ **B.** by explaining what to do if you see a tornado
 ◉ **C.** by describing a tornado and explaining how tornadoes form
 ◯ **D.** by listing the wind speeds of tornadoes

2. Why is the town of Water Valley, Ohio, mentioned in the introduction?

 ◉ **F.** to get the reader's attention
 ◯ **G.** to explain the illustration
 ◯ **H.** to explain the caption
 ◯ **J.** to understand the title

3. Which text feature helps you picture the subject?

 ◯ **A.** the introduction
 ◉ **B.** the illustration
 ◯ **C.** the title
 ◯ **D.** the caption

4. What does the caption tell you?

 ◯ **F.** how the people of Water Valley felt
 ◉ **G.** how a tornado forms
 ◯ **H.** how a thundercloud forms
 ◯ **J.** what the wind speed is in a tornado

5. What can you learn from the title?

 ◯ **A.** that the passage is about Water Valley
 ◉ **B.** that the passage is about tornadoes
 ◯ **C.** that the passage is about clouds
 ◯ **D.** that the passage is about storms

Syllabication

Choose the correct way to divide each underlined word into syllables.

1. We heard the sound of <u>thunder</u>.
   - ○ **A.** thun • der
   - ○ **B.** thund • er
   - ○ **C.** thu • nder
   - ○ **D.** th • un • der

2. The plane flew into the eye of the <u>hurricane</u>.
   - ○ **F.** hur • ric • ane
   - ○ **G.** hurr • i • cane
   - ○ **H.** hurri • cane
   - ○ **J.** hur • ri • cane

3. This <u>climate</u> is very rainy.
   - ○ **A.** clim • ate
   - ○ **B.** cli • ma • te
   - ○ **C.** cli • mate
   - ○ **D.** cl • im • ate

4. The tornado was the town's worst <u>tragedy</u>.
   - ○ **F.** tra • ge • dy
   - ○ **G.** trag • e • dy
   - ○ **H.** tra • gedy
   - ○ **J.** tra • ged • y

5. She saw two broken <u>radios</u> in the middle of the street.
   - ○ **A.** rad • i • os
   - ○ **B.** ra • di • os
   - ○ **C.** ra • d • ios
   - ○ **D.** r • adi • os

STOP

Name _____

Spelling Spell Long *a*, Long *e*, and Long *i*

Find the correctly spelled word to complete each sentence.
Fill in the circle beside your answer.

1. It was such a _____ day that my friends and I took a long walk.
   - ○ **A.** mighld
   - ○ **B.** mild
   - ○ **C.** mield
   - ○ **D.** myld

2. We followed a path covered with pine _____.
   - ○ **F.** needles
   - ○ **G.** neadles
   - ○ **H.** nedles
   - ○ **J.** neddles

3. Each _____ I took made a slight crackling sound.
   - ○ **A.** streighd
   - ○ **B.** streid
   - ○ **C.** stride
   - ○ **D.** stried

4. I could see the top of the pine tree _____ in the breeze.
   - ○ **F.** swae
   - ○ **G.** swai
   - ○ **H.** sweigh
   - ○ **J.** sway

5. I also found a beautiful maple _____ on the ground.
   - ○ **A.** leef
   - ○ **B.** lief
   - ○ **C.** leif
   - ○ **D.** leaf

STOP

Vocabulary Dictionary: Guide Words

Read each question. Fill in the circle next to the best answer.

1. Which set of guide words might appear at the top of a dictionary page on which the word *sketch* is found?
   - ● **A.** skate/skew
   - ○ **C.** skipper/skunk
   - ○ **B.** skit/skull
   - ○ **D.** skirt/skittle

2. Which set of guide words might appear at the top of a dictionary page on which the word *damage* is found?
   - ○ **F.** dabble/dainty
   - ● **H.** daily/dangle
   - ○ **G.** daybreak/dealer
   - ○ **J.** damp/daring

3. Which set of guide words might appear at the top of a dictionary page on which the word *cumulus* is found?
   - ○ **A.** cube/cuff
   - ○ **C.** cycle/cylinder
   - ● **B.** culture/curb
   - ○ **D.** couple/cucumber

4. Which set of guide words might appear at the top of a dictionary page on which the word *monsoon* is found?
   - ● **F.** monorail/monster
   - ○ **H.** mood/morning
   - ○ **G.** monkey/monopoly
   - ○ **J.** month/monument

5. Which set of guide words might appear at the top of a dictionary page on which the word *earthquake* is found?
   - ○ **A.** each/eagle
   - ○ **C.** earnings/earphone
   - ○ **B.** ear/earthly
   - ● **D.** early/earthworm

Name _____

Grammar Conjunctions

Choose the word that best completes each sentence. Fill in the circle next to the best answer.

1. The volcano showed signs of becoming active, _____ people began to leave their homes.
   - ○ **A.** but
   - ○ **B.** or
   - ○ **C.** and
   - ○ **D.** except

2. Maria's family was rushing to the car _____ Maria ran to get her dog.
   - ○ **F.** if
   - ○ **G.** since
   - ○ **H.** nor
   - ○ **J.** when

3. Maria had to go back for Petey _____ he was left in the back yard.
   - ○ **A.** but
   - ◉ **B.** since
   - ○ **C.** or
   - ○ **D.** and

4. She carried Petey to the car _____ he was scared by the volcano's noise.
   - ◉ **F.** because
   - ○ **G.** except
   - ○ **H.** only
   - ○ **J.** but

5. Maria's family got away safely, _____ they had to leave behind many of their possessions.
   - ○ **A.** if
   - ◉ **B.** but
   - ○ **C.** or
   - ○ **D.** when

Name _____

Grammar Compound Sentences

Choose the compound sentence. Then fill in the circle next to the best answer.

1. ○ **A.** Scientists, who had watched the volcano for months, said that it could erupt at any time.
   ○ **B.** When the volcano finally erupted, emergency workers were prepared.
   ◉ **C.** A cloud of ashes rose from the crater, and lava poured down the side of the mountain.
   ○ **D.** The people in nearby towns loaded their belongings into their cars. Then they drove to safety.

2. ○ **F.** My mother, who grew up on a farm, once experienced a huge blizzard.
   ○ **G.** The biting wind and heavy snow made it difficult to see.
   ◉ **H.** My grandfather tried to open the barn door, but it was blocked by a snowdrift.
   ○ **J.** Luckily, the cows and pigs in the barn had enough food to survive.

3. ○ **A.** When spring arrives, we often have hailstorms in my state.
   ◉ **B.** The hail pours down in sheets, and it batters cars and houses.
   ○ **C.** Hail and rain usually occur in a heavy thunderstorm.
   ○ **D.** Hail stones, which can be as large as baseballs, can do a great deal of damage.

Go on

4. ○ **F.** The storm chasers wait for tornadoes to strike. Then they follow them.

○ **G.** As soon as storm clouds gather, the storm chasers get ready to move.

○ **H.** The storm chasers, who are experts on tornadoes, try to learn more about the storms.

◉ **J.** They get as close to a tornado as possible, and they gather information about the storm.

5. ◉ **A.** A lightning storm is an awesome sight, but it is also very dangerous.

○ **B.** If you are outside during a lightning storm, don't take shelter under a large tree.

○ **C.** Large trees, which attract lightning, can endanger people with falling branches.

○ **D.** It is best to stay indoors or inside a vehicle during a lightning storm.

Writing Skills Capitalizing and Punctuating Sentences

Choose the sentence that is capitalized and punctuated correctly. Fill in the circle next to the best answer.

1. ● **A.** Mt. Washington is known for its extreme weather.
   ○ **B.** winds of 75 miles per hour are common.
   ○ **C.** When do the winds reach maximum speed.
   ○ **D.** Ranger Station is at the top of the mountain?

2. ○ **F.** the volcano on the small island erupted.
   ○ **G.** The hot orange lava rolled slowly toward the sea
   ● **H.** A helicopter flew near the crater.
   ○ **J.** Mr. Wright took spectacular photographs of the sight?

3. ○ **A.** the tornado was coming closer to Jamie's home.
   ○ **B.** Jamie and her parents hurried to a nearby closet?
   ○ **C.** Jamie's mother brought a flashlight and a radio
   ● **D.** Jamie could hear the tornado howling outside her house.

4. ○ **F.** The snow skiers huddled together on the side of the mountain?
   ○ **G.** the blizzard had caught them by surprise.
   ● **H.** Who knew when the storm would end?
   ○ **J.** pike's Peak could be very dangerous in the winter.

5. ● **A.** The Boy Scouts paddled their canoes down the swollen river.
   ○ **B.** It was flowing much more quickly than last year's canoe trip,
   ○ **C.** Suddenly the lead boat tipped over?
   ○ **D.** two boys were thrown into the water, but they reached the bank unharmed.

Nature's Fury

Level 5, Theme 1: Week 3

Weekly Skills Test Record

Student _____   Date _____

Student Record Form	Possible Score	Criterion Score	Student Score
A: Categorize and Classify	5	4	
B: Information and Study Skills Using Graphic Aids: Maps, Globes, Charts, Tables, and Graphs	5	4	
C: Word Roots *struct* and *rupt*	5	4	
D: Spelling The /o͞o/ Sound, the /yo͞o/ Sound, the Long *o* Sound	5	4	
E: Vocabulary Dictionary: Definitions	5	4	
F: Grammar Singular and Plural Nouns	5	4	
G: Grammar More Plural Nouns	5	4	
H: Writing Skills Correcting Sentence Fragments	5	4	
TOTAL	40	32	
Total Student Score x 2.5 =			%

Name _____

Categorize and Classify

Read each passage. Then read each question and fill in the circle next to the best answer.

Group rescues animals from flood waters

During last week's flood in Denton, Pennsylvania, a group of people worked together to save several animals from the rising waters. Five wildlife photographers who were visiting the area organized the rescue effort. The photographers called on game wardens and neighbors to join the search for animals.

First, they rescued a deer trapped on an island created by the floodwaters. Later in the day, they moved five rabbits and three raccoons to higher ground. Lisa Bellows, one of the photographers, said, "We also saved a mother and baby squirrel. I took some great photographs of them for my collection."

---

1. Based on the passage, in which category do deer, rabbits, and raccoons belong?

   ○ **A.** animals rescued from an island
   ○ **B.** animals photographed by Lisa Bellows
   ◉ **C.** animals rescued from the flood
   ○ **D.** animals not moved to higher ground

2. Based on the passage, which of the following do **not** fit into the category of people who rescued the animals?

   ○ **F.** game wardens
   ○ **G.** neighbors
   ○ **H.** photographers
   ◉ **J.** park rangers

Go on ⇨

Lyndsey's Vacation

As the storm moved across the coastal town of Rockport, the rain fell harder and harder. Lyndsey couldn't believe that this was happening during her family's vacation. It was the first time they had ever visited a beach town.

Lyndsey heard the roar of the wind and the sound of heavy rain. She listened to the small hotel creak with the force of the strong wind. Mom did not look up from the book she was reading. Dad watched television. Carl, Lyndsey's brother, listened to music through earphones.

Lyndsey looked out the window and saw a branch fall from the tree in the yard and puddles on the sidewalk. As she watched, the wind blew an old soda can past the window. Lyndsey felt sad.

At last the sun came out. Lyndsey and Carl threw on their bathing suits and ran outside. They splashed in the puddles and looked at the colorful flowers in the yard of the hotel. Then they went to the beach to meet their mom and dad.

Lyndsey decided it wasn't such a bad day after all.

3. Based on the passage, which category includes these things: wind, heavy rain, creaking?

   ○ **A.** things near the hotel
   ○ **B.** things on television
   ◉ **C.** things Lyndsey hears
   ○ **D.** things Carl listens to

4. Based on the passage, which category includes these things: branch, puddles, soda can?

   ○ **F.** things near the beach
   ◉ **G.** things Lyndsey sees
   ○ **H.** things Carl sees
   ○ **J.** things Dad reads about in the newspaper

5. Based on the passage, which category includes these things: splashing in puddles and looking at flowers?

   ○ **A.** things that Carl did
   ○ **B.** things that Lyndsey did
   ◉ **C.** things that Lyndsey and Carl did
   ○ **D.** things that the entire family did

STOP

Name _____

Information and Study Skills
Using Graphic Aids: Maps, Globes, Charts, Tables, and Graphs

Look at the chart below. Then read each question and fill in the circle next to the best answer.

Once a hurricane forms, it is rated in one of five categories on the Saffir-Simpson Hurricane Scale. Here are the categories:

Category	Wind Speed	Effects
1	74–95 mph	Some flooding but generally no damage to buildings
2	96–110 mph	Lots of trees down and minor damage to roofs
3	111–130 mph	Structural damage in houses and destruction of mobile homes; severe flooding
4	131–155 mph	Some roofs ripped off, major damage to buildings
5	greater than 155 mph	Huge damage to most wooden structures

Use the chart to answer these questions. Fill in the circle next to the best answer.

1. According to the chart, how many categories of hurricanes are there?
   - ○ **A.** four
   - ◉ **B.** five
   - ○ **C.** six
   - ○ **D.** seven

2. What are the wind speeds in a Category 2 hurricane?
   - ◉ **F.** 96–110 mph
   - ○ **G.** 111–130 mph
   - ○ **H.** 131–155 mph
   - ○ **J.** greater than 155 mph

3. Which of the following may happen in a Category 3 hurricane?
   - ◉ **A.** Mobile homes may be destroyed.
   - ○ **B.** All the buildings in an area may be damaged.
   - ○ **C.** Most homes are destroyed.
   - ○ **D.** Trees are blown over.

4. Which category of hurricane has wind speeds between 111–130 mph?
   - ○ **F.** Category 1
   - ○ **G.** Category 2
   - ◉ **H.** Category 3
   - ○ **J.** Category 4

5. Which of the following may happen in a Category 5 hurricane?
   - ○ **A.** Buildings are not generally damaged.
   - ◉ **B.** Wooden buildings are greatly damaged.
   - ○ **C.** Many trees are blown down.
   - ○ **D.** Roofs may blow off.

Name _____

Word Roots *struct* and *rupt*

Choose the correct meaning for each underlined word. Fill in the circle next to the best answer.

1. The <u>construction</u> of the new dam will begin in August.
   - ○ **A.** building
   - ○ **B.** tearing down
   - ○ **C.** changing
   - ○ **D.** moving

2. The safety <u>instructions</u> said not to talk on the phone during a thunderstorm.
   - ○ **F.** a book that tells about storms
   - ○ **G.** a type of phone
   - ○ **H.** someone who writes about safety
   - ◉ **J.** a list of steps telling how to do or make something

3. The pipe suddenly <u>ruptured</u>, and water poured into the room.
   - ○ **A.** fell over
   - ○ **B.** rolled away
   - ◉ **C.** broke apart
   - ○ **D.** filled up

4. The earthquake caused widespread <u>destruction</u>.
   - ○ **F.** panic
   - ◉ **G.** damage
   - ○ **H.** tremors
   - ○ **J.** sadness

5. The news of the storm <u>interrupted</u> my favorite program.
   - ◉ **A.** broke into
   - ○ **B.** turned off
   - ○ **C.** came after
   - ○ **D.** came at an early hour

STOP

Name _____

Spelling The /o͞o/ Sound, the /yo͞o/ Sound, the Long *o* Sound

Find the correctly spelled word to complete each sentence.
Fill in the circle beside your answer.

1. A raccoon _____ my sandwich.

   ○ **A.** stowl   ◉ **C.** stole

   ○ **B.** stol   ○ **D.** stohl

2. I was thankful to see my _____ group gathered near the picnic benches.

   ◉ **F.** youth   ○ **H.** yuoth

   ○ **G.** yuth   ○ **J.** yooth

3. Some friends invited me on a _____ through the woods.

   ◉ **A.** stroll   ○ **C.** strole

   ○ **B.** stroal   ○ **D.** stroul

4. We obeyed the _____ and stayed close together on our walk.

   ◉ **F.** rules   ○ **H.** roles

   ○ **G.** rools   ○ **J.** rooles

5. We laughed because we were in such a happy _____.

   ○ **A.** muud   ◉ **C.** mood

   ○ **B.** moode   ○ **D.** moud

Name _____

Vocabulary Dictionary: Definitions

Read the dictionary entry and the questions that follow. Decide which meaning of the word *glass* is used in each sentence. Fill in the circle next to the best answer.

glass (glăs), *n.* **1.** A hard, clear material that is used to make windows and lenses: *The computer screen is made of glass.* **2.** A container to drink from made of glass: *He filled a glass with water.* **3.** The amount a glass can hold: *Pour a glass of milk into the bowl.* **4.** A mirror: *He stared at his reflection in the glass.*

1. *She studied her face in the glass.*
   - ○ **A.** definition 1
   - ○ **B.** definition 2
   - ○ **C.** definition 3
   - ◉ **D.** definition 4

2. *He drank lemonade from a tall glass.*
   - ○ **F.** definition 1
   - ◉ **G.** definition 2
   - ○ **H.** definition 3
   - ○ **J.** definition 4

3. *She polished the rock until it was as smooth as glass.*
   - ◉ **A.** definition 1
   - ○ **B.** definition 2
   - ○ **C.** definition 3
   - ○ **D.** definition 4

4. *Add a glass of broth to each pot.*
   - ○ **F.** definition 1
   - ○ **G.** definition 2
   - ◉ **H.** definition 3
   - ○ **J.** definition 4

5. *Allan looked through the glass into the house.*
   - ◉ **A.** definition 1
   - ○ **B.** definition 2
   - ○ **C.** definition 3
   - ○ **D.** definition 4

Name _____

Grammar Singular and Plural Nouns

Choose the sentence in which correct plural nouns are used. Fill in the circle next to the best answer.

1. ○ **A.** The reporter turned in two storys about the weather.
   ○ **B.** She wrote that volcanos are awesome eventes.
   ○ **C.** She said that high windes could rip branchs off trees.
   ◉ **D.** Her articles were printed in two newspapers.

2. ○ **F.** Scientistes are working to learn more about volcanoes.
   ◉ **G.** Volcano eruptions can produce huge masses of lava.
   ○ **H.** The streames of hot lava can flow down into valleyes.
   ○ **J.** Ashs from a large eruption can darken the skys for miles around.

3. ○ **A.** High winds from hurricanes cause damage to beachs each year.
   ○ **B.** Hurricane season is especially bad for residentes of Florida.
   ◉ **C.** Major hurricanes often damage or destroy many homes and businesses.
   ○ **D.** Some citys have been hit by hurricans several times.

4. ◉ **F.** Our teachers have made lots of speeches about tornado safety.
   ○ **G.** Many schooles practice tornado drilles each spring.
   ○ **H.** When an alarm sounds, everyone quickly files into hallwayes or basementes.
   ○ **J.** Then students sit on the floor and place their handes over their heads.

5. ○ **A.** One of Carla's hobbys is studying tornadoes.
   ◉ **B.** She has collected boxes of stories about these storms.
   ○ **C.** In her searchs, she has gone to several librarys.
   ○ **D.** Carla is determined to keep her friendes and neighbores safe.

Grammar More Plural Nouns

Find the correctly spelled plural to complete each sentence. Fill in the circle beside your answer.

1. Most _____ are reluctant to live close to a volcano.
   - ○ **A.** peoples
   - ○ **B.** person
   - ○ **C.** peoplies
   - ◉ **D.** people

2. They listen to their _____ when an eruption occurs.
   - ○ **F.** radioes
   - ◉ **G.** radios
   - ○ **H.** radioyes
   - ○ **J.** radio

3. Falling _____ often cover everything nearby.
   - ○ **A.** azhes
   - ○ **B.** ashs
   - ○ **C.** ashis
   - ◉ **D.** ashes

4. Animals such as deer and _____ have to find new places to live.
   - ○ **F.** wolfes
   - ○ **G.** wolfs
   - ◉ **H.** wolves
   - ○ **J.** wulves

5. Even tiny animals such as _____ are affected by volcanic eruptions.
   - ◉ **A.** mice
   - ○ **B.** mouses
   - ○ **C.** myce
   - ○ **D.** mices

STOP

Name _____

Writing Skills Correcting Sentence Fragments

Choose the group of words that is a complete, correctly written sentence. Fill in the circle next to your answer.

1. ○ **A.** Had no way of knowing that a storm was coming.
   ○ **B.** Felt a few raindrops falling.
   ◉ **C.** Then hail began to fall from the sky.
   ○ **D.** The car and roof.

2. ◉ **F.** The earthquake shook the house.
   ○ **G.** Glasses and plates from the shelves.
   ○ **H.** Fell down all around us.
   ○ **J.** The Smith's house on the corner.

3. ○ **A.** The day the dam on the Harris River broke.
   ○ **B.** To rebuild some of the neighborhoods.
   ○ **C.** New rules from the government about flooding.
   ◉ **D.** Many people had to leave their homes behind.

4. ○ **F.** The strong winds from the thunderstorm.
   ◉ **G.** Jamaal's dad pulled the car off the road.
   ○ **H.** Waited until the storm died down.
   ○ **J.** The flashing lightning and the driving rain.

5. ◉ **A.** Cindy trudged through the huge drifts of snow.
   ○ **B.** Snowflakes that were like large white feathers.
   ○ **C.** Waved her arms up and down to stay warm.
   ○ **D.** Had rarely seen so much snow in one storm.

Give It All You've Got

Level 5, Theme 2: Week 1

Weekly Skills Test Record

Student _____   Date _____

Student Record Form

	Possible Score	Criterion Score	Student Score
A: Fact and Opinion	5	4	
B: Compound Words	5	4	
C: Spelling Compound Words	5	4	
D: Vocabulary Word Families	5	4	
E: Grammar Common and Proper Nouns	5	4	
F: Grammar Possessive Nouns	5	4	
TOTAL	30	24	
Total Student Score x 3.33 =			%

Fact and Opinion

Read the passage. Then read each question and fill in the circle next to the best answer.

Clementine Hunter, Artist

Clementine Hunter was born in Louisiana in 1885. As a girl, she picked cotton on a large farm called a plantation. As an adult, she worked in the plantation's laundry and kitchen. Although her work was difficult, Clementine enjoyed watching the things that happened around her. She loved to see people dancing and girls picking flowers. She watched children playing and dogs wagging their tails. It seemed that she saw interesting sights everywhere she looked.

One day a visitor to the plantation left behind some old tubes of paint. Clementine wanted to try out the paints, but she didn't have anything to paint on. She began to search for something to use as a canvas. Soon she found a window shade in the trash. In no time, she had created a charming painting on the shade.

Clementine was in her fifties when this happened. Even though she loved to paint, she could not take formal art lessons. This didn't stop her. She began to paint whenever she got the chance. She painted lively scenes of people cooking food, playing games, and getting married. She painted on paper bags, scraps of wood, bottles, and even on old pots. When she died at the age of 101, she had created over 4,000 paintings.

Over the years people in nearby communities began to hear about Clementine's paintings. She became the first African-American painter to show her artwork at the New Orleans Museum of Art. Today, many experts feel that her paintings are the work of an extremely talented artist. Some even feel that she was as skilled as a well-known painter named Grandma Moses. People who collect her paintings believe that she is one of the best painters ever.

1. Which of the following statements is an opinion?
    - ○ **A.** Clementine picked cotton as a young girl.
    - ○ **B.** Clementine began painting when she was in her fifties.
    - ◉ **C.** Clementine was an extremely talented artist.
    - ○ **D.** Clementine used a window shade to make her first painting.

2. Which of the following statements is a fact?
    - ◉ **F.** Clementine died at the age of 101.
    - ○ **G.** Clementine's first painting was charming.
    - ○ **H.** It seemed that Clementine saw interesting sights everywhere she looked.
    - ○ **J.** Clementine is one of the best painters ever.

3. How do you know that the following statement is a fact?

    Clementine was the first African-American painter to display her work at the New Orleans Museum of Art.
    - ○ **A.** The author is reliable.
    - ◉ **B.** The statement can be proven.
    - ○ **C.** Detailed information is given.
    - ○ **D.** The statement is easy to believe.

4. Which of these statements is an opinion?
    - ○ **F.** Clementine painted on paper bags, scraps of wood, bottles, and even on old pots.
    - ○ **G.** When she died, Clementine had created over 4,000 paintings.
    - ○ **H.** Clementine was born in Louisiana in 1885.
    - ◉ **J.** Clementine was as skilled as Grandma Moses.

5. Which word in this sentence signals an opinion?

    People who collect her paintings believe that she is one of the best painters ever.
    - ○ **A.** People
    - ○ **B.** collect
    - ◉ **C.** believe
    - ○ **D.** ever

    STOP

Name _____

Compound Words

Choose the compound word that has the same meaning as the underlined part of each sentence. Fill in the circle next to the best answer.

1. My father took <u>a tool that shines light</u> on our night hike.
- ○ **A.** lantern
- ○ **B.** flashlight
- ○ **C.** light bulb
- ○ **D.** candle

2. We left the tent before <u>the sun came up</u>.
- ○ **F.** morning
- ○ **G.** sunset
- ○ **H.** sunrise
- ○ **J.** dusk

3. I put a <u>tool I use to brush my teeth</u> in my pocket.
- ○ **A.** brush
- ○ **B.** toothbrush
- ○ **C.** toothpick
- ○ **D.** dental floss

4. We planned to walk to the park ranger's <u>main office</u>.
- ○ **F.** headlight
- ○ **G.** store
- ○ **H.** lodge
- ○ **J.** headquarters

5. When we got there, my father bought a <u>paper with the day's news</u>.
- ○ **A.** newspaper
- ○ **B.** newsprint
- ○ **C.** newscast
- ○ **D.** magazine

STOP

Spelling Compound Words

**Find the correctly spelled word to complete each sentence.
Fill in the circle beside your answer.**

1. In this booklet you will find an _____ schedule of fair events.
   - ○ **A.** up-to date
   - ◉ **C.** up-to-date
   - ○ **B.** up to date
   - ○ **D.** upto date

2. _____ is encouraged to enter several events.
   - ◉ **F.** Everybody
   - ○ **H.** Everybodie
   - ○ **G.** Everbody
   - ○ **J.** Everybode

3. Most of the children's events will take place during the _____ hours.
   - ○ **A.** daylite
   - ◉ **C.** daylight
   - ○ **B.** daylit
   - ○ **D.** dalight

4. The winner of the contest for the best jam and jelly will receive a _____ quilt.
   - ○ **F.** hadmade
   - ○ **H.** handmaid
   - ◉ **G.** handmade
   - ○ **J.** handmead

5. The children will also get a chance to ride the _____.
   - ○ **A.** merry go round
   - ○ **C.** merry-go round
   - ○ **B.** merry go-round
   - ◉ **D.** merry-go-round

Vocabulary Word Families

Read the choices. Decide which word is not related to the others. Fill in the circle next to the best answer.

1. ○ **A.** divide
   ○ **B.** division
   ○ **C.** dividend
   ◉ **D.** divers

2. ○ **F.** number
   ◉ **G.** nimble
   ○ **H.** numerous
   ○ **J.** numeral

3. ○ **A.** study
   ○ **B.** student
   ○ **C.** studious
   ◉ **D.** stuck

4. ◉ **F.** locksmith
   ○ **G.** locate
   ○ **H.** dislocate
   ○ **J.** location

5. ○ **A.** portable
   ○ **B.** import
   ◉ **C.** portrait
   ○ **D.** transport

Grammar Common and Proper Nouns

Fill in the circle next to the sentence that is written correctly.

1. ○ **A.** My aunt, who lives in roanoke, Virginia, loves to travel.
   ◉ **B.** Last year she took a trip to Texas and New Mexico.
   ○ **C.** She visited a mission in San antonio and a pueblo in Santa fe.
   ○ **D.** She liked the swimming in the gulf of Mexico best of all.

2. ◉ **F.** Aunt Gwen saw the bats fly out of Carlsbad Caverns.
   ○ **G.** She went to the balloon festival in albuquerque.
   ○ **H.** She watched the hot air balloons drift over sandia peak.
   ○ **J.** The sunset over the sangre de cristo mountains was deep pink.

3. ○ **A.** My uncle martin, who lives in London, England, loves to come to the United States.
   ○ **B.** On his first visit, he toured the white house in washington, D.C.
   ◉ **C.** He loves to visit the Smoky Mountains in North Carolina.
   ○ **D.** Watching the wildlife come to feed at sunset at cades cove is his favorite activity.

4. ○ **F.** Uncle Martin also likes to go tubing down little River.
   ○ **G.** He enjoys hiking through newfound Gap.
   ○ **H.** Last year he climbed to the top of clingman's dome.
   ◉ **J.** Once he climbed the rocks behind Eagle Falls and got all wet.

5. ○ **A.** My favorite vacation place is walt Disney world in Orlando, florida.
   ◉ **B.** Walt Disney World has been so popular that the company built parks in Paris, France, and Tokyo, Japan.
   ○ **C.** I love to visit all the different countries' exhibits in epcot center.
   ○ **D.** My family went there for new year's eve a few years ago.

Name _____

Grammar Possessive Nouns

Fill in the circle next to the sentence that is written correctly.

1. ○ **A.** There is a rock climber's convention at the arena.
    ○ **B.** A women's club for climbers passed out flyers at the door.
    ○ **C.** Childrens' competitions for rock climbing are lots of fun.
    ○ **D.** The sports' appeal seems to be growing each year.

2. ○ **F.** Over 500 people have signed up to run in the Womens' 5K Run on Saturday.
    ○ **G.** I love to hear the sound of hundreds of runner's feet at the start of the race.
    ○ **H.** The runners will help raise money for the communitys' children.
    ○ **J.** Some of the money will be used to buy children's books for the library.

3. ○ **A.** The coache's conference was held last month.
    ○ **B.** One athletes' speech lasted two hours.
    ○ **C.** The meeting for men's soccer was a big success.
    ○ **D.** One teams' coach brought T-shirts for all.

4. ○ **F.** My two brother's softball team is going to the state tournament.
    ○ **G.** Their head coach's goal is to win the championship.
    ○ **H.** The players received pointers from a college womens' team.
    ○ **J.** Peoples' expectations for the team are very high.

5. ○ **A.** Several country's best dog-sled drivers are signed up for the race.
    ○ **B.** All the driver's sleds have been packed and checked.
    ○ **C.** The men's division of the race will begin tomorrow morning.
    ○ **D.** Our citys' volunteers will make sure the course is safe.

Give It All You've Got

Level 5, Theme 2: Week 2

Weekly Skills Test Record

Student _____   Date _____

Student Record Form	Possible Score	Criterion Score	Student Score
A: Story Structure	5	4	
B: Information and Study Skills Select the Appropriate Reference Source	5	4	
C: Word Roots *spec/t* and *opt*	5	4	
D: Spelling The /ou/ Sound, the /ô/ Sound, and the /oi/ Sound	5	4	
E: Vocabulary Dictionary: Multiple-Meaning Words	5	4	
F: Grammar Action Verbs	5	4	
G: Grammar Direct Objects	5	4	
H: Writing Skills Paraphrasing	5	4	
TOTAL	40	32	
Total Student Score x 2.5 =			%

Story Structure

Read the passage. Then read each question and fill in the circle next to the best answer.

The Recital

Chad finished playing his favorite piece on the piano. Then he looked up at his piano teacher.

"How lovely, Chad! I can tell that you've been practicing," exclaimed Mrs. Franklin. "Now, I have a surprise for you. In two weeks, we're going to have a recital at the Parkdale Library. You'll be able to play your song for your family. The other students and their families will attend, too."

On the way home Chad kicked a stone from the path. He thought about how awful it would be to play in front of other people. "I just don't think I can do it," he decided.

That afternoon Chad asked his sister Cara to help him think of a way to get out of the recital. "It won't be so bad," she told him. Then she invited him to come with her to the library.

After they had been there awhile, Cara said, "Let's go find the piano. As many times as I've been here, I've never seen it." The librarian directed them to a room on the second floor.

The shiny, black piano was the most beautiful one Chad had ever seen. As he ran his hand lightly over the keys, Cara sat down in a chair. "Go ahead, Chad. Just pretend that I'm not even here," she urged.

Chad began playing. Within minutes he was carried away by the beautiful sound of the instrument. When he finished, Cara's clapping startled him. Later, Chad and Cara stopped at the drugstore. Mr. Turner, who owned the store, greeted them. His daughter, Melissa, was one of Mrs. Franklin's students.

"Chad, I can't wait to hear you play at the recital," said Mr. Turner. Chad looked at Cara. He thought about the piano and how much his mother and father would enjoy hearing him play it.

"Thanks," replied Chad. "I think you'll really like the piece I've chosen to play."

1. Who is the main character in this story?
   - ○ **A.** Mrs. Franklin
   - ○ **B.** Mr. Turner
   - ○ **C.** Cara
   - ◉ **D.** Chad

2. What problem does Chad have?
   - ○ **F.** He doesn't want to go to the library with Cara.
   - ◉ **G.** He feels nervous about his piano recital.
   - ○ **H.** He doesn't like his piano teacher.
   - ○ **J.** He has not practiced his piano piece enough.

3. Who helps Chad solve his problem?
   - ◉ **A.** Cara
   - ○ **B.** Mrs. Franklin
   - ○ **C.** Chad's mother
   - ○ **D.** Melissa

4. Where does Chad solve his problem?
   - ○ **F.** at Chad's school
   - ◉ **G.** in the library
   - ○ **H.** on the way home from his lesson
   - ○ **J.** in Cara's bedroom

5. Which is the first **important** event?
   - ○ **A.** Chad walks home.
   - ◉ **B.** Mrs. Franklin tells Chad about the recital.
   - ○ **C.** Chad kicks a stone.
   - ○ **D.** Cara invites Chad to the library.

Name _____

Information and Study Skills
Select the Appropriate Reference Source

Read each question and fill in the circle next to the best answer.

1. Which of these would you use if you needed to find a friend's address?
   - ○ **A.** Thesaurus
   - ○ **B.** Encyclopedia
   - ○ **C.** Atlas
   - ◉ **D.** Telephone Directory

2. Which of these would you use if you wanted to find out who won gold medals in the Olympic Games in 1972?
   - ○ **F.** Dictionary
   - ◉ **G.** Almanac
   - ○ **H.** Atlas
   - ○ **J.** Thesaurus

3. Which of these would you use to find out where China is located?
   - ◉ **A.** Atlas
   - ○ **B.** Telephone Directory
   - ○ **C.** Encyclopedia
   - ○ **D.** Dictionary

4. Which of these would you use to look up the pronunciation of the word *icicle*?
   - ◉ **F.** Dictionary
   - ○ **G.** Almanac
   - ○ **H.** Encyclopedia
   - ○ **J.** Thesaurus

5. Which of these would you use to find a word that is the opposite in meaning of the word *stroll*?
   - ○ **A.** Dictionary
   - ○ **B.** Atlas
   - ◉ **C.** Thesaurus
   - ○ **D.** Almanac

Name _____

Word Roots *spec/t* and *opt*

Choose the correct meaning for each underlined word.
Fill in the circle next to the best answer.

1. Before the race the coach <u>inspects</u> the track.
   - ○ **A.** looks at carefully
   - ○ **B.** runs around
   - ○ **C.** quickly cleans up
   - ○ **D.** smoothes out

2. Heat waves rising from the track create an <u>optical</u> illusion.
   - ○ **F.** having to do with vision
   - ○ **G.** having to do with runners
   - ○ **H.** interesting
   - ○ **J.** happening over and over

3. The <u>spectators</u> cheer as the runners cross the finish line.
   - ○ **A.** coaches for a winning team
   - ○ **B.** people who keep scores
   - ○ **C.** people who watch an event
   - ○ **D.** athletes who compete

4. Mr. Vegas cannot see the scores without his <u>spectacles</u>.
   - ○ **F.** scoreboards
   - ○ **G.** words
   - ○ **H.** camera
   - ○ **J.** eyeglasses

5. Mr. Vegas decides to see an <u>optician</u> the next day.
   - ○ **A.** a person who fills orders for medicine
   - ○ **B.** a person who checks people's eyes
   - ○ **C.** a person who assists a doctor
   - ○ **D.** a person who fixes people's bones

Name _____

Spelling The /ou/ Sound, the /ô/ Sound, and the /oi/ Sound

Find the correctly spelled word to complete each sentence.
Fill in the circle beside your answer.

1. We are expecting almost a _____ people at the fair.
   ○ **A.** thousend   ○ **C.** thowsand
   ◉ **B.** thousand   ○ **D.** thoosand

2. The area around the game booths is always very _____.
   ○ **F.** noeesy   ◉ **H.** noisy
   ○ **G.** nossy   ○ **J.** noesy

3. Children can choose their prizes from _____ of stuffed animals.
   ◉ **A.** mounds   ○ **C.** monds
   ○ **B.** mownds   ○ **D.** maunds

4. If you get thirsty from playing games, you can _____ at the snack booth for a cold drink.
   ○ **F.** paws   ○ **H.** poss
   ◉ **G.** pause   ○ **J.** paase

5. The fair is always a success because of our _____ supporters.
   ○ **A.** loal   ◉ **C.** loyal
   ○ **B.** loyel   ○ **D.** loil

Vocabulary Dictionary: Multiple-Meaning Words

Read the definitions and the sentences that follow. Decide which definition fits the meaning of the underlined word in the sentence. Fill in the circle next to the best answer.

stand (stănd) *v.* ***stood, standing*** **1.** To support oneself on the feet in an upright position. **2.** To be in a certain place. *n.* **3.** A strongly held position on an issue. **4.** A small structure for selling goods.

1. My cousin works in a hot-dog <u>stand</u> next to the bowling alley.
    - ○ **A.** definition 1
    - ○ **B.** definition 2
    - ○ **C.** definition 3
    - ◉ **D.** definition 4

2. The congresswoman's <u>stand</u> on raising taxes is widely known.
    - ○ **F.** definition 1
    - ○ **G.** definition 2
    - ◉ **H.** definition 3
    - ○ **J.** definition 4

3. Some of the fans had to <u>stand</u> for the entire game.
    - ◉ **A.** definition 1
    - ○ **B.** definition 2
    - ○ **C.** definition 3
    - ○ **D.** definition 4

board (bôrd) *v.* ***boarded, boarding*** **1.** To climb onto a vehicle or vessel. **2.** To cover up with something such as boards. *n.* **3.** A piece of sawed lumber. **4.** A group of people that oversees a company or activity.

4. My father and I had to <u>board</u> up the windows of the old house.
    - ○ **F.** definition 1
    - ◉ **G.** definition 2
    - ○ **H.** definition 3
    - ○ **J.** definition 4

5. My aunt is a member of the <u>board</u> for Alton Industries.
    - ○ **A.** definition 1
    - ○ **B.** definition 2
    - ○ **C.** definition 3
    - ◉ **D.** definition 4

STOP

Grammar Action Verbs

Read the sentences in each question. Choose the sentence that does NOT contain an action verb. Fill in the circle beside the best answer.

1. ○ **A.** Aunt Lorraine is my favorite relative.
   ○ **B.** She walks four miles every day.
   ○ **C.** She reads at least four books each month.
   ○ **D.** She plays tennis with me every week.

2. ○ **F.** Our soccer team kicks hundreds of practice balls each day.
   ○ **G.** The team also runs a mile before each practice.
   ○ **H.** The team wins most of the games it competes in.
   ○ **J.** Each member of the team is a good player.

3. ○ **A.** Eric listens to music each morning while getting ready for school.
   ○ **B.** He dances when his favorite songs are playing.
   ○ **C.** He is not the best dancer in the world.
   ○ **D.** His sisters laugh when they see him dancing.

4. ○ **F.** Cassie studied all evening for her science test.
   ○ **G.** The next day Mr. Wang handed a test to each student.
   ○ **H.** Cassie nervously bit her nails.
   ○ **J.** She was scared she would fail.

5. ○ **A.** Liza rides horses at her grandparents' farm.
   ○ **B.** Her favorite horse is Mr. Major.
   ○ **C.** Mr. Major gallops faster than the other horses.
   ○ **D.** He sails over the hedges with Liza on his back.

Grammar Direct Objects

**Read each group of sentences. Choose the sentence that does
NOT contain a direct object. Fill in the circle beside the best answer.**

1. ○ **A.** Alison hit the ball into the field.
   ◉ **B.** Alison ran around the bases.
   ○ **C.** Matt caught the ball in his glove.
   ○ **D.** Matt held the ball in the air.

2. ○ **F.** Rudy played the drums in the school band concert.
   ◉ **G.** All the students in the band were sad that night.
   ○ **H.** Afterwards, each student shook the director's hand.
   ○ **J.** The director will start another job next school year.

3. ○ **A.** Can you see the lead runner?
   ○ **B.** The runners passed the big oak tree.
   ○ **C.** Coach Myers just waved his arms.
   ◉ **D.** Daniel is in front of the other runners!

4. ○ **F.** Edward shot the basketball from the three-point line.
   ○ **G.** No one else shot the ball better that night.
   ◉ **H.** He played better than he ever has before.
   ○ **J.** Edward won the game for our team!

5. ◉ **A.** Dusk came quickly for the students in the canoes.
   ○ **B.** They paddled the canoes toward the campground.
   ○ **C.** Everyone ate hamburgers grilled on the campfire.
   ○ **D.** Then they sang songs until bedtime.

Writing Skills Paraphrasing

Read each paragraph and answer the questions that follow. Fill in the circle next to the best answer.

The members of the basketball team gathered in the locker room before the big game. They greeted one another quietly. Suzanne felt a knot in the pit of her stomach. Her palms were sweaty. The coach came in and the players looked at each other. The coach said, "We're going to win this one for sure!"

1. Which of these best restates how Suzanne felt?
   - ○ **A.** Her stomach felt odd.
   - ○ **B.** She was worried about her sweaty palms.
   - ◉ **C.** She was nervous.
   - ○ **D.** She wished the other players would speak loudly.

2. In paraphrasing the above paragraph, what information would you **not** include?
   - ○ **F.** The players gathered in the locker room.
   - ◉ **G.** The players looked at each other.
   - ○ **H.** It was the day of a big game.
   - ○ **J.** The coach was sure the team would win.

Jonathan works at the community library on Saturdays. He helps people choose books and checks the books out. He also straightens the shelves and enters information into the computer. His favorite part of the job is discussing books with the library's visitors.

3. Which of these best combines the ideas in the passage?
   - ○ **A.** Jonathan does various jobs at the library on Saturdays.
   - ○ **B.** Jonathan's favorite job at the library is talking about books.
   - ○ **C.** Jonathan sometimes enters information in the library's computer.
   - ○ **D.** Jonathan helps visitors to the library choose books.

Go on ▷

4. Which of these best restates how Jonathan feels about working at the library?

- ○ **F.** He doesn't like his job.
- ○ **G.** He is shy and stays away from visitors.
- ○ **H.** He likes his job and especially likes talking with visitors.
- ○ **J.** He hopes to quit his job soon.

5. In paraphrasing the above paragraph, what information would you **not** include?

- ○ **A.** Jonathan works at the library.
- ○ **B.** Jonathan works on Saturdays.
- ○ **C.** Jonathan does various jobs at the library.
- ○ **D.** The library is down the street from Jonathan's home.

Give It All You've Got

Level 5, Theme 2: Week 3

Weekly Skills Test Record

Student _____ Date _____

Student Record Form	Possible Score	Criterion Score	Student Score
A: Predicting Outcomes	5	4	
B: Suffixes -*ward* and -*ous*	5	4	
C: Spelling The /ôr/ Sound, the /âr/ Sound, and the /är/ Sound	5	4	
D: Vocabulary Homophones	5	4	
E: Grammar Main/Helping Verbs	5	4	
F: Grammar Linking Verbs	5	4	
G: Writing Skills Combining Sentences with Helping Verbs	5	4	
TOTAL	35	28	
Total Student Score x 2.86 =			%

Predicting Outcomes

Read the passage. Then read each question and fill in the circle next to the best answer.

Counting to Five

Both Lisa and Charlotte had brown hair and green eyes. They were both friendly, and they liked the same subjects in school. Both girls played soccer and liked to swim. If one girl tried something new, the other one always tried it, too. The main difference between the two girls was that Lisa was sometimes less patient than Charlotte.

One day before soccer practice, Lisa and Charlotte went swimming at the recreation center. While they were there, Lisa decided that she wanted to jump off the high diving board. She had jumped off the low board many times, but the high board had always scared her. Charlotte had never jumped from the high board either. "I know I can do it," Lisa said to herself.

Lisa told Charlotte what she planned to do. Then she slowly climbed the ladder while Charlotte watched. She walked nervously to the end of the board and looked down. The water seemed to be miles below. For just a minute, she thought about going back down the ladder. Then she decided that it might be easier if she closed her eyes.

From the ground, Charlotte saw Lisa squeeze her eyes shut, then open them quickly. "It's too scary to do this with my eyes closed," Lisa yelled to Charlotte. "I wouldn't know when I was going to hit the water."

"I know a trick," Charlotte called back. "Try counting very slowly to five. That always helps me do scary things."

Lisa began to count. "One. . . Two. . . Three. . . ." On the third count, Lisa leapt from the board and splashed into the water. When she came to the surface, she was laughing. "Oh, Charlotte, that was so much fun! From now on, I'll always count when I try something new. Only I'll always have to stop at three because I'm not as patient as you are."

1. What does Lisa probably say to Charlotte after the story ends?
   - ○ **A.** "Let's have a snack."
   - ◉ **B.** "Now, you try it."
   - ○ **C.** "The water feels great."
   - ○ **D.** "You're more patient."

2. Which of these will Charlotte probably do the next time she tries something new?
   - ○ **F.** hold her breath
   - ○ **G.** close her eyes
   - ○ **H.** hold Lisa's hand
   - ◉ **J.** count to five

3. Which sentence from the story might help readers predict that Lisa won't count all the way to five before jumping?
   - ○ **A.** They were on the same soccer team, and they both liked to swim.
   - ○ **B.** From the ground, Charlotte saw Lisa squeeze her eyes shut, then open them quickly.
   - ◉ **C.** The main difference between the two girls was that Lisa was sometimes less patient than Charlotte.
   - ○ **D.** "From now on, I'll always count when I try something new."

4. Which detail from the story helps readers predict that Lisa will find the courage to jump off the board?
   - ◉ **F.** She says, "I know I can do it."
   - ○ **G.** She walks slowly to the end of the board.
   - ○ **H.** The water looks like it's miles below her.
   - ○ **J.** She closes her eyes before she jumps.

5. Which lesson from your own experience might have helped you predict that Lisa would find the courage to jump off the high board?
   - ◉ **A.** A good friend can help you to be brave.
   - ○ **B.** It's fun to do things with a good friend.
   - ○ **C.** Good friends are hard to find.
   - ○ **D.** You can share your problems with a friend.

Name _____

Suffixes *-ward* and *-ous*

Choose the correct meaning for each underlined word.
Fill in the circle next to the best answer.

1. My brother was <u>envious</u> when I got new soccer shoes.
   - ○ **A.** full of envy
   - ○ **B.** wanting envy
   - ○ **C.** the opposite of envy
   - ○ **D.** without envy

2. I kicked the ball <u>upward</u>, and it sailed over the fence.
   - ○ **F.** the opposite of up
   - ○ **G.** without moving up
   - ○ **H.** not moving up
   - ○ **J.** moving up

3. The shopkeeper was <u>furious</u> when the ball broke a window.
   - ○ **A.** the opposite of fury
   - ○ **B.** without fury
   - ○ **C.** full of fury
   - ○ **D.** having little fury

4. My <u>adventurous</u> aunt went river rafting last summer.
   - ○ **F.** without adventure
   - ○ **G.** full of adventure
   - ○ **H.** afraid of adventure
   - ○ **J.** the opposite of adventure

5. Brightly colored leaves drifted <u>downward</u> on the chilly fall day.
   - ○ **A.** moving down
   - ○ **B.** the opposite of down
   - ○ **C.** not moving down
   - ○ **D.** without moving down

STOP

Name _____

Spelling The /ôr/ Sound, the /âr/ Sound, and the /är/ Sound

Find the correctly spelled word to complete each sentence.
Fill in the circle beside your answer.

1. The decorations for the booths show Lara's _____ for using color.
   - ○ **A.** flayre
   - ○ **B.** flaire
   - ○ **C.** flare
   - ◑ **D.** flair

2. One booth has a _____ at each corner.
   - ◑ **F.** torch
   - ○ **G.** tawrch
   - ○ **H.** torche
   - ○ **J.** tourch

3. At another booth, children can watch an _____ draw pictures.
   - ○ **A.** artest
   - ◑ **B.** artist
   - ○ **C.** airtest
   - ○ **D.** ortist

4. They can also watch adults _____ animal figures from bars of soap.
   - ○ **F.** carrve
   - ○ **G.** cawrve
   - ◑ **H.** carve
   - ○ **J.** caurve

5. Most children enjoy trying to win the giant stuffed _____.
   - ○ **A.** bare
   - ○ **B.** bar
   - ○ **C.** bair
   - ◑ **D.** bear

Name _____

Vocabulary Homophones

Read the sentences. Decide which word best completes the sentence. Fill in the circle next to the best answer.

1. The scratch on my hand took three days to _____.
   - A. he'll
   - B. heel
   - C. hele
   - **D. heal**

2. Please hand me a _____, a hammer, and a nail.
   - F. bored
   - G. boored
   - H. boared
   - **J. board**

3. Our dance teacher told us to _____ partners.
   - A. chews
   - **B. choose**
   - C. chose
   - D. chooze

4. The letter that we _____ yesterday came back today.
   - F. scent
   - G. cent
   - **H. sent**
   - J. sint

5. All day Jennifer walked around in a _____.
   - **A. daze**
   - B. dais
   - C. days
   - D. dase

STOP

Name _____

Grammar Main/Helping Verbs

**Read the sentences. Choose the sentence that does NOT contain
a helping verb. Fill in the circle next to the best answer.**

1. ○ **A.** Erica is climbing the steepest trail.
    ○ **B.** She will go to the very highest peak.
    ◐ **C.** She wants a photograph of the valley below.
    ○ **D.** Has she ever made the climb before?

2. ○ **F.** Grady is going to the art fair.
    ○ **G.** He will take two of his oil paintings.
    ○ **H.** His teacher is judging the competition.
    ◐ **J.** Most of his classmates attend the fair every year.

3. ○ **A.** Zoe is babysitting her two baby sisters tonight.
    ○ **B.** Their parents are attending a charity benefit.
    ○ **C.** The sisters can watch several Disney movies without tiring.
    ◐ **D.** Zoe enjoys the movies, too.

4. ○ **F.** Are you swimming in the weekend competition?
    ○ **G.** I am swimming in the butterfly event.
    ◐ **H.** The coach wants me to compete in the free-style event, too.
    ○ **J.** He has already entered me in both events.

5. ◐ **A.** Blue is my favorite color.
    ○ **B.** I am helping my mother paint my room today.
    ○ **C.** We are painting the walls light blue and the trim white.
    ○ **D.** We will finish painting this evening.

Name _____

Grammar Linking Verbs

Follow the directions. Then fill in the circle next to the best answer.

1. Choose a sentence that does **not** contain a linking verb.
    - ○ **A.** Sal is an experienced hiker.
    - ○ **B.** She still feels nervous before hikes.
    - ○ **C.** She will talk to the group this evening.
    - ○ **D.** Sal is not a nervous speaker.

2. Choose a sentence that contains a predicate noun.
    - ○ **F.** Hoover will lead the group hike on Saturday.
    - ○ **G.** He plans to leave from Lookout Point.
    - ○ **H.** He is an expert on the plants of the region.
    - ○ **J.** He tells the hikers about animals, too.

3. Choose a sentence that contains a predicate adjective.
    - ○ **A.** Hillary was frightened by reports of a bear near the campground.
    - ○ **B.** She decided to find out how truthful the reports were.
    - ○ **C.** She spoke to a park ranger stationed near the canyon.
    - ○ **D.** He told her not to worry.

4. Choose a sentence that contains a predicate noun.
    - ○ **F.** Mr. West is a ranger at the park.
    - ○ **G.** He gives lectures on park subjects.
    - ○ **H.** People enjoy his enthusiastic talks.
    - ○ **J.** They leave knowing much more about park plants and animals.

5. Choose a sentence that contains a predicate adjective.
    - ○ **A.** Madison took photographs of the park flowers.
    - ○ **B.** The colors of the flowers were brilliant.
    - ○ **C.** She entered her best photographs in a school contest.
    - ○ **D.** One of them won a first-place ribbon.

Go on ▷

Vocabulary Combining Sentences with Helping Verbs

Choose the best way to combine each pair of sentences.
Fill in the circle next to your answer.

1. Lucy had washed her face. She had brushed her teeth.
   - ● **A.** Lucy had washed her face and brushed her teeth.
   - ○ **B.** Lucy had washed her face and Lucy had brushed her teeth.
   - ○ **C.** Lucy had washed her face, brushed her teeth.
   - ○ **D.** Lucy had washed her face, she had brushed her teeth.

2. My brother Randy could drive us to the movie. He could see the movie with us.
   - ○ **F.** My brother Randy could drive us to the movie, and he could see the movie with us.
   - ○ **G.** My brother Randy could drive us to the movie and then could see the movie with us.
   - ○ **H.** My brother Randy could drive us to the movie and could see the movie with us.
   - ● **J.** My brother Randy could drive us to the movie and see the movie with us.

3. My sister will cook dinner. She will help me study my spelling words.
   - ○ **A.** My sister will cook dinner and will help me study my spelling words.
   - ● **B.** My sister will cook dinner and help me study my spelling words.
   - ○ **C.** My sister will cook dinner, and she will help me study my spelling words.
   - ○ **D.** My sister will cook dinner, she will help me study my spelling words.

4. Mrs. Nguyen is opening the store early. She is giving out free candy to the children.

- ○ **F.** Mrs. Nguyen is opening the store early and giving out free candy to the children.
- ○ **G.** Mrs. Nguyen is opening the store early and is giving out free candy to the children.
- ○ **H.** Mrs. Nguyen is opening the store early, she is giving out free candy to the children.
- ○ **J.** Mrs. Nguyen is opening the store early and then is giving out free candy to the children.

5. I can ride my bike to the store. I can bring home some milk.

- ○ **A.** I can ride my bike to the store, and then can bring home some milk.
- ○ **B.** I can ride my bike to the store, and I can bring home some milk.
- ○ **C.** I can ride my bike to the store and bring home some milk.
- ○ **D.** I can ride my bike to the store and can bring home some milk.

STOP

Give It All You've Got

Level 5, Theme 2: Week 4

Weekly Skills Test Record

Student _____ Date _____

Student Record Form

	Possible Score	Criterion Score	Student Score
A: Topic, Main Idea, and Supporting Details	5	4	
B: Suffixes -ive and -ic	5	4	
C: Spelling The /îr/ Sound, the /ûr/ Sound	5	4	
D: Vocabulary Syllables in a Dictionary	5	4	
E: Grammar Verb Tenses	5	4	
F: Grammar More About Verb Tenses	5	4	
TOTAL	30	24	
Total Student Score x 3.33 =			%

Topic, Main Idea, and Supporting Details

Read the passage. Then read each question and fill in the circle next to the best answer.

How to Clean Your Room

Cleaning a room doesn't have to be a hard or boring job. In fact, there are many ways to make this task easy and fun.

Listening to music can add fun to work. Before you start to clean your room, turn on a radio or put on your favorite CD. Be sure to choose music that has a lively beat. This will brighten your mood, and it will help the time go by quickly.

Picking up the trash in your room is a good place to start. This step is really quite easy. First, find a wastebasket or paper bag. Moving in time to the music, go around the room and pick up all the trash. When you finish, empty the wastebasket into a trash can.

Putting large objects away will make a room appear cleaner. Look around and find the four largest objects that need to be put away. Put these objects where they belong. In an instant your room will seem neater and your job smaller.

Next, put everything that is out of place into piles. You might place all the clothes in one pile, all the toys in another, and all the books and magazines in another. Plan ahead as you do this. That is, put the pile of toys near the toy box and the pile of clothes near the closet. Don't forget to sing along to the music while you work.

Finally, go through each pile and put everything where it belongs. Put the dirty clothes in the clothes hamper and hang up the clean clothes. Neatly arrange the books on the book shelf and put the toys in the toy box. Last, take a quick look around to be sure that you didn't forget anything. Be proud of a job well done.

1. What is the topic of this passage?
   - ○ **A.** how to pick up trash while moving to music
   - ○ **B.** how to have fun while putting things in piles
   - ◉ **C.** how to clean up a room and have fun
   - ○ **D.** how to find four large objects in a messy room

2. Which sentence from the passage states the main idea of the second paragraph?
   - ◉ **F.** Listening to music can add fun to work.
   - ○ **G.** Before you start to clean your room, turn on a radio or put on your favorite CD.
   - ○ **H.** Be sure to choose music that has a lively beat.
   - ○ **J.** This will brighten your mood, and it will help the time go by quickly.

3. Which detail supports the idea that picking up trash is a good place to begin?
   - ○ **A.** This step is really quite easy.
   - ○ **B.** Put the toys in the toy box.
   - ○ **C.** Be sure not to forget anything.
   - ○ **D.** Cleaning a room doesn't have to be boring.

4. Which detail supports the idea that cleaning your room can be fun?
   - ○ **F.** Find a wastebasket or paper bag.
   - ◉ **G.** Don't forget to sing along as you work.
   - ○ **H.** Take a quick look around to be sure that you didn't forget anything.
   - ○ **J.** Be proud of a job well done.

5. Which sentence from the passage states the main idea of the fourth paragraph?
   - ○ **A.** Look around and find the four largest objects that need to be put away.
   - ○ **B.** Put these objects where they belong.
   - ○ **C.** In an instant your room will seem neater and your job smaller.
   - ◉ **D.** Putting large objects away will make a room appear cleaner.

STOP

Suffixes *-ive* and *-ic*

Choose the correct meaning for each underlined word.
Fill in the circle next to the best answer.

1. Larry is a <u>creative</u> painter.
   - ○ **A.** having the ability to create
   - ○ **B.** without the ability to create
   - ○ **C.** learning how to create
   - ○ **D.** one who is unable to create

2. Our <u>poetic</u> parrot loves to make up rhymes.
   - ○ **F.** unlike a poet
   - ○ **G.** like a poet
   - ○ **H.** unable to be a poet
   - ○ **J.** without a poet

3. The house has an <u>expansive</u> view of the valley.
   - ○ **A.** expanding upward
   - ○ **B.** not expanding
   - ○ **C.** expanding in all directions
   - ○ **D.** expanding very little

4. My <u>athletic</u> brother can run, jump, and swim.
   - ○ **F.** unable to be an athlete
   - ○ **G.** with an athlete
   - ○ **H.** unlike an athlete
   - ○ **J.** like an athlete

5. Wren is an <u>expressive</u> speaker.
   - ○ **A.** lacking the ability to express ideas clearly
   - ○ **B.** having the ability to express ideas clearly
   - ○ **C.** being filled with ideas to express clearly
   - ○ **D.** one who has the ability to express ideas clearly

STOP

Name _____

Spelling The /îr/ Sound, the /ûr/ Sound

Find the correctly spelled word to complete each sentence.
Fill in the circle beside your answer.

1. A _____ from the crowd could be heard when the winner of the drawing was announced.
   - ○ **A.** chair
   - ○ **B.** chear
   - ○ **C.** cher
   - ◉ **D.** cheer

2. The winner of the drawing will receive a _____ necklace.
   - ○ **F.** paerl
   - ○ **G.** purl
   - ◉ **H.** pearl
   - ○ **J.** pirol

3. The necklace is _____ a lot of money.
   - ◉ **A.** worth
   - ○ **B.** wirth
   - ○ **C.** werth
   - ○ **D.** wearth

4. _____ events have been planned especially for the children.
   - ○ **F.** Certon
   - ◉ **G.** Certain
   - ○ **H.** Curtain
   - ○ **J.** Sertain

5. Children may _____ paint on a large poster board near the wading pool.
   - ◉ **A.** smear
   - ○ **B.** smeer
   - ○ **C.** smeir
   - ○ **D.** smere

Name _____

Vocabulary Syllables in a Dictionary

Read each dictionary entry. Circle the answer choice with the correct stress.

1. as • ter • oid (as′ tə roid′) *n.* One of many small planets that orbit the sun.
   - ○ **A.** AS/te/roid
   - ○ **B.** as/TE/roid
   - ○ **C.** as/TER/oid
   - ○ **D.** as/te/ROID

2. ap • pli • cant (ap′ li kənt) *n.* A person who applies for something.
   - ○ **F.** AP/pli/cant
   - ○ **G.** ap/pli/CANT
   - ○ **H.** ap/PLI/cant
   - ○ **J.** ap/PLIC/ant

3. i • mag • i • na • tion (i maj′ ə na′ shən) *adj.* The ability of the brain to picture things that are not real.
   - ○ **A.** I/mag/i/na/tion
   - ○ **B.** i/MAG/i/na/tion
   - ○ **C.** i/mag/i/NA/tion
   - ○ **D.** i/mag/i/na/TION

4. per • pet • u • al (pər pĕch′ o͞o əl) *adj.* Lasting forever.
   - ○ **F.** PER/pet/u/al
   - ○ **G.** per/PET/u/al
   - ○ **H.** per/pet/U/al
   - ○ **J.** per/pet/u/AL

5. in • tel • li • gent (ĭn tĕl′ ə jənt) *adj.* Smart or bright.
   - ○ **A.** in/tel/LI/gent
   - ○ **B.** IN/tel/li/gent
   - ○ **C.** in/tel/li/GENT
   - ○ **D.** in/TEL/li/gent

Name _____

Grammar Verb Tenses

Fill in the circle next to the sentence that is written correctly.

1. ○ **A.** Last month my sister and I will learn a new sport.
   ◉ **B.** We watched our friends at the skating rink two weeks ago.
   ○ **C.** Next week I rent two pairs of ice skates.
   ○ **D.** Yesterday my sister and I nervously glide onto the ice.

2. ○ **F.** Last year I like to ride my bike to school.
   ○ **G.** Next week, my friend Juan rode with me.
   ◉ **H.** We will park our bikes outside our school's entrance.
   ○ **J.** Last week, we will plan to hurry home to play baseball.

3. ○ **A.** Our school sponsored a soccer tournament next week.
   ◉ **B.** Many teams from our area will attend.
   ○ **C.** Next week, our school team hoped to win the championship.
   ○ **D.** We will win the championship last year.

4. ○ **F.** Mario moves into his new house last weekend.
   ○ **G.** He will attend his new school yesterday.
   ○ **H.** He enjoys meeting his classmates then.
   ◉ **J.** He thinks he will like his new home and school.

5. ○ **A.** Jeff and Jim will make a big yellow kite yesterday.
   ○ **B.** They flew the kite in the park tomorrow.
   ○ **C.** Many of their friends will made kites, too.
   ◉ **D.** Tomorrow the sky will be filled with kites.

Name _____

Grammar More About Verb Tenses

Read the sentences and answer the questions.
Fill in the circle next to the best answer.

1. Which sentence has a verb in the past tense?
   - ○ **A.** Next month I will play in my first table tennis tournament.
   - ○ **B.** I practice playing table tennis every afternoon.
   - ○ **C.** Last week, I defeated my sister in table tennis for the first time.
   - ○ **D.** A year from now, I will be in lots of table tennis tournaments.

2. Which sentence has a verb in the future tense?
   - ○ **F.** I will take my first trumpet lesson next month.
   - ○ **G.** I listen to trumpet music every day.
   - ○ **H.** Last month, I bought a CD of trumpet music by Louis Armstrong.
   - ○ **J.** I like the trumpet more than any other instrument.

3. Which sentence has a verb in the present tense?
   - ○ **A.** Twyla planted daffodil bulbs last spring.
   - ○ **B.** She grows lots of different flowers in her garden.
   - ○ **C.** Next spring, Twyla's daffodils will bloom as bright yellow flowers.
   - ○ **D.** Twyla helped me plant some bulbs in my yard.

4. Which sentence has a verb in the future tense?
   - ○ **F.** Terrell's uncle designed a new miniature computer.
   - ○ **G.** Terrell's father also works in the computer field.
   - ○ **H.** He gives Terrell the latest programs for his home computer.
   - ○ **J.** Terrell will study computer science in college someday.

5. Which sentence has a verb in the present tense?
   - ○ **A.** Heidi and Sam buy lots of books about the planets and stars.
   - ○ **B.** They once looked through a powerful telescope.
   - ○ **C.** Yesterday they took a trip to the planetarium.
   - ○ **D.** Tomorrow Heidi will write a report about their visit.

STOP

Voices of the Revolution

Level 5, Theme 3: Week 1

Weekly Skills Test Record

Student _____   Date _____

Student Record Form

	Possible Score	Criterion Score	Student Score
A: Author's Viewpoint	5	4	
B: Possessives and Contractions	5	4	
C: Spelling Final /ər/	5	4	
D: Vocabulary Synonyms	5	4	
E: Grammar Subject-Verb Agreement	5	4	
F: Grammar Regular and Irregular Verbs	5	4	
G: Writing Skills Using Exact Nouns and Verbs	5	4	
TOTAL	35	28	
Total Student Score x 2.86 =			%

Author's Viewpoint

Read the passage. Then read each question and fill in the circle next to the best answer.

Sybil Ludington

On a cold night in 1777, two thousand British soldiers attacked the town of Danbury, Connecticut. Danbury was very important to the colonial army because it was a storage place for food, clothing, and medicine. Unfortunately, only 150 colonial soldiers were available to defend the town. The small army needed help!

A messenger quickly left on horseback to ask Colonel Henry Ludington to bring more troops. However, when the rider arrived at Ludington's farm, he learned that Ludington's men had gone home.

Who could round up the soldiers in the dead of night? Ludington thought of his 16-year-old daughter, Sybil. He knew she could do this dangerous job. In an instant, Sybil saddled her horse Star and rode into the frozen dark. She bravely galloped from farm to farm. She followed twisting, muddy roads across the countryside. Along the way, she shouted the news of the attack. She warned families to be ready to flee if the British should come their way.

Sybil arrived home early the next morning. When she got there she saw more than 400 men preparing to leave for the twenty-five-mile journey to Danbury. Colonel Ludington was very grateful that she had helped.

Today, people remember Sybil's courageous ride. A statue of Sybil and Star stands in the town of Carmel, Connecticut. Sybil has also been honored by having her picture on a postage stamp.

Go on

1. What is the author's viewpoint in this article?
   - ○ **A.** Sybil's ride was the most important event in the American Revolution.
   - ○ **B.** Ludington's soldiers should have been ready for battle.
   - ○ **C.** Sybil was too young to make such a dangerous ride.
   - ◉ **D.** Sybil Ludington's bravery helped the colonial soldiers.

2. Which statement reflects the author's opinion?
   - ○ **F.** Sybil Ludington was a very brave girl.
   - ○ **G.** Danbury was a storage place for food, clothing, and medicine.
   - ○ **H.** More than 400 men went to help the troops in Danbury.
   - ○ **J.** A statue of Sybil and Star stands in the town of Carmel.

3. How do you know that the following statement is a fact, and not the author's viewpoint?

   On a cold night in 1777, two thousand British soldiers attacked the town of Danbury, Connecticut.
   - ○ **A.** The author is reliable.
   - ◉ **B.** The statement can be proven.
   - ○ **C.** Detailed information is given.
   - ○ **D.** The statement is easy to believe.

4. Why did the author most likely write this article?
   - ○ **F.** to entertain the reader with a story about a girl and a horse
   - ◉ **G.** to inform the reader about events during the colonial period
   - ○ **H.** to describe the Connecticut countryside
   - ○ **J.** to persuade the reader to visit the statue of Sybil

5. Which of these phrases shows that the author respects Sybil Ludington?
   - ○ **A.** shouted the news
   - ○ **B.** muddy roads
   - ◉ **C.** dangerous job
   - ○ **D.** twenty-five-mile journey

Name _____

Possessives and Contractions

Choose the word or words that mean about the same as the underlined part of each sentence. Fill in the circle next to the best answer.

1. <u>We'll</u> visit the scene of the Boston Tea Party.
    - ○ **A.** We would
    - ● **C.** We will
    - ○ **B.** We could
    - ○ **D.** We still

2. The guide said, "Next, <u>you're</u> going aboard that ship."
    - ○ **F.** your
    - ○ **H.** you sure
    - ○ **G.** you are
    - ○ **J.** you our

3. The <u>colonists'</u> costumes included feathers.
    - ○ **A.** colonist is
    - ○ **B.** colonist has
    - ○ **C.** colonist does
    - ○ **D.** belonging to the colonists

4. The British <u>soldier's</u> uniform was red.
    - ○ **F.** belonging to the soldier
    - ○ **G.** soldier has
    - ○ **H.** soldier does
    - ○ **J.** soldier is

5. The <u>patriot's</u> about to begin his speech.
    - ○ **A.** patriot has
    - ○ **B.** patriot is
    - ○ **C.** belonging to the patriot
    - ○ **D.** patriot was

Name _____

Spelling Final /ər/

Find the correctly spelled word to complete each sentence.
Fill in the circle beside your answer.

1. The daughter of the _____ of Lexington was married.
   - ○ **A.** mayer
   - ○ **B.** mayir
   - ○ **C.** mayor
   - ○ **D.** mayier

2. The guests gathered in the _____.
   - ○ **F.** parlor
   - ○ **G.** parlur
   - ○ **H.** parlar
   - ○ **J.** parler

3. The bride glanced over her _____ at her mother.
   - ○ **A.** shouldar
   - ○ **B.** shouldur
   - ○ **C.** shoulder
   - ○ **D.** shouldor

4. Her mother was seated by a _____ ringed with flowers.
   - ○ **F.** piller
   - ○ **G.** pillar
   - ○ **H.** pillor
   - ○ **J.** pillur

5. The bride's brother, a _____, arrived just in time.
   - ○ **A.** sailer
   - ○ **B.** saler
   - ○ **C.** sailur
   - ○ **D.** sailor

STOP

Name _____

Vocabulary Synonyms

Read each sentence. Choose the word that means the same as the underlined word. Fill in the circle next to the best answer.

1. The old trunk was <u>cherished</u> by the family.
   - ○ **A.** opened
   - ○ **B.** moved
   - ○ **C.** stored
   - ◐ **D.** loved

2. Mrs. Harrison kept <u>cloth</u> in the trunk.
   - ○ **F.** clothes
   - ◐ **G.** fabric
   - ○ **H.** books
   - ○ **J.** odds and ends

3. Like the furnishings in the house, the trunk was <u>plain</u>.
   - ◐ **A.** simple
   - ○ **B.** heavy
   - ○ **C.** fancy
   - ○ **D.** broken

4. The British soldiers <u>pushed</u> past the woman into the house.
   - ○ **F.** rolled
   - ○ **G.** skipped
   - ○ **H.** strolled
   - ◐ **J.** shoved

5. She grew <u>uneasy</u> when the soldiers opened the trunk.
   - ○ **A.** difficult
   - ○ **B.** angry
   - ◐ **C.** nervous
   - ○ **D.** cautious

STOP

Name _____

Grammar Subject-Verb Agreement

Choose the sentence that is written correctly. Fill in the circle next to the best answer.

1. ○ **A.** The colonists wants freedom.
   ○ **B.** King George refuse to grant them certain rights.
   ◉ **C.** He places a tax on tea.
   ○ **D.** I knows that this is not fair.

2. ○ **F.** The colonists does not like the tax on tea.
   ○ **G.** Three ships am filled with tea in Boston Harbor.
   ◉ **H.** Patriots climb aboard the ships at night.
   ○ **J.** They throws the tea into the water.

3. ◉ **A.** Paul Revere rides his horse through the countryside at night.
   ○ **B.** He make the ride on April 18, 1775.
   ○ **C.** The people is warned that British soldiers have landed.
   ○ **D.** Revere and the colonists is determined to win the fight.

4. ○ **F.** Paul Revere were made even more famous by a poem.
   ◉ **G.** The poem is by Henry Wadsworth Longfellow.
   ○ **H.** Its words am familiar to every school child.
   ○ **J.** The poem tell the story of Paul Revere's famous ride.

5. ○ **A.** Paul Revere do many different jobs during the Revolutionary War.
   ○ **B.** For example, he print the paper money for the colony.
   ◉ **C.** All his jobs require a great deal of skill.
   ○ **D.** Many colonists sees the examples of his work.

Grammar Regular and Irregular Verbs

Fill in the circle next to the sentence that is written correctly.

1. ○ **A.** Paul Revere gave the message to the farmers.
   ○ **B.** Who gived Paul such a message?
   ○ **C.** John gaved it to him yesterday.
   ○ **D.** All the farmers have gaven the message to their friends.

2. ○ **F.** The patriot runned away from the soldiers.
   ○ **G.** The patriot had ran into the secret meeting.
   ○ **H.** The soldiers had ranned after him.
   ◉ **J.** He has run from the soldiers several times.

3. ○ **A.** Colonists fighted in the Revolutionary War for many reasons.
   ◉ **B.** They fought to win their freedom from England.
   ○ **C.** Many had fight because of high taxes.
   ○ **D.** People foughted in hopes of a better life.

4. ○ **F.** A colonist forgetted to warn his neighbor.
   ○ **G.** British soldiers had forget to search their houses.
   ◉ **H.** The colonist forgot to hide his secret papers.
   ○ **J.** The soldiers had forgotted who he was.

5. ◉ **A.** The woman gave a speech to a group of patriots.
   ○ **B.** Her words had gived the others new hope.
   ○ **C.** She has givened all her time for the cause.
   ○ **D.** The crowd gaved her a round of applause.

Name _____

Writing Skills Using Exact Nouns and Verbs

Replace each underlined noun or verb with a more exact word.
Fill in the circle next to your answer.

1. Abigail Adams placed a vase of white <u>flowers</u> on her desk.
   - ○ **A.** roses
   - ○ **B.** plants
   - ○ **C.** stems
   - ○ **D.** leaves

2. A sea gull <u>flew</u> high over the ships in Boston's harbor.
   - ○ **F.** went
   - ○ **G.** moved
   - ○ **H.** dropped
   - ○ **J.** soared

3. The colonist <u>held</u> the secret document tightly to his chest.
   - ○ **A.** pulled
   - ○ **B.** clutched
   - ○ **C.** tipped
   - ○ **D.** pushed

4. Paul Revere's horse <u>ran</u> along the dark road at top speed.
   - ○ **F.** walked
   - ○ **G.** hurried
   - ○ **H.** went
   - ○ **J.** galloped

5. The soldier <u>talked</u> to be heard above the booming cannons.
   - ○ **A.** shouted
   - ○ **B.** whispered
   - ○ **C.** sang
   - ○ **D.** spoke

STOP

Voices of the Revolution

Level 5, Theme 3: Week 2

Weekly Skills Test Record

Student _____ Date _____

Student Record Form

	Possible Score	Criterion Score	Student Score
A: Cause and Effect	5	4	
B: Information and Study Skills Primary and Secondary Sources	5	4	
C: Syllabication VCCV and VCV Patterns	5	4	
D: Spelling VCCV and VCV Patterns	5	4	
E: Vocabulary Dictionary: Pronunciation Key	5	4	
F: Grammar Verb Phrases with *have*	5	4	
G: Grammar *teach/learn, let/leave, sit/set, can/may*	5	4	
H: Writing Skills Capitalizing Names of People and Places	5	4	
TOTAL	40	32	
Total Student Score x 2.5 =			

Name _____

Cause and Effect

Read the passage. Then read each question and fill in the circle next to the best answer.

Just Like Father

Jeremy watched as his father poured the British soldier a drink of water. The soldier hurriedly drank the water and left. "A simple 'Thank you' would have been nice," Jeremy thought grumpily.

Jeremy's father owned an inn in Boston. Months earlier, King George had decided to send soldiers from England to the colonies. The king had ordered the colonists to provide the soldiers food and housing. As a result, Jeremy's father worked very hard. In return for this work, he received only a little money from the city.

After the British soldier drank the water, he walked into the street to join his regiment for inspection. Each morning every soldier had to shave, powder his hair with flour, and polish his boots. Soldiers who did not pass inspection were punished.

As the soldier walked along, a colonist ran by shouting angrily, "Go home, Redcoat!" Most colonists hated having British soldiers in their towns. The soldiers' presence made the tension between England and the colonies worse.

The soldier grumbled, "I hate this job! The colonists hate me, and I have to wear this hot and itchy red jacket. For this, I only get paid eight pence a day! I wish I was back in London!"

When the soldier returned to the inn that evening, Jeremy was struck by the very sad expression on the soldier's face. Instead of a soldier in uniform, Jeremy saw a human being with feelings. "Good evening, sir," Jeremy said.

The warm greeting lifted the soldier's spirits. Jeremy and the soldier began to talk. The soldier told Jeremy about the son he had left behind in London. Later, when Jeremy went to bed, he thought about the British soldiers. "They're men struggling to make their way, just like Father," he decided.

Go on

1. Why did Jeremy's father provide food and housing for British soldiers?
    - ○ **A.** King George offered to pay him well for several rooms at the inn.
    - ◉ **B.** King George ordered the colonists to provide the soldiers room and board.
    - ○ **C.** King George asked all innkeepers in Boston to help the British soldiers.
    - ○ **D.** King George sent Jeremy's father a letter asking him for his help.

2. Why did the colonist shout at the British soldier to go home?
    - ○ **F.** The British soldier didn't thank Jeremy's father for the drink of water.
    - ○ **G.** The British soldier didn't have his boots polished.
    - ◉ **H.** The British soldiers' presence made the tensions in Boston worse.
    - ○ **J.** The British soldier didn't like his job.

3. For British soldiers, which was an effect of not passing inspection?
    - ◉ **A.** They were punished.
    - ○ **B.** They were fired.
    - ○ **C.** They were forced to work in an inn.
    - ○ **D.** They had to apologize to a British officer.

4. Which of these was an effect of the conversation between Jeremy and the soldier?
    - ○ **F.** Jeremy began to hate British soldiers.
    - ○ **G.** Jeremy wanted to become a British soldier.
    - ◉ **H.** Jeremy began to understand the British soldiers.
    - ○ **J.** Jeremy became angry with his father.

5. Which of these was a reason that the British soldier did not like his job?
    - ○ **A.** He did not like being in Boston.
    - ○ **B.** He did not like carrying a gun.
    - ○ **C.** He did not like not going to school.
    - ◉ **D.** He did not get much money.

Name _____

Information and Study Skills
Primary and Secondary Sources

Read each question. Then answer the question by finding the correct item. Fill in the circle next to the best answer.

1. Which of the following is a primary source about the Boston Tea Party?

    ○ **A.** a letter by one of the patriots who threw the tea into the water
    ○ **B.** a book about the Boston Tea Party
    ○ **C.** a movie about the Boston Tea Party
    ○ **D.** a textbook with a picture of the tea being thrown into the water

2. Which of the following is a secondary source about Paul Revere's ride?

    ○ **F.** Paul Revere's diary
    ○ **G.** a newspaper article describing the ride
    ○ **H.** a book about Paul Revere's life
    ○ **J.** a letter written by a friend of Paul Revere

3. Which of the following is a secondary source about the uniform of the British soldier?

    ○ **A.** a letter from the tailor who designed the uniform
    ○ **B.** a book by an expert on British uniforms
    ○ **C.** a 1775 drawing of a British uniform
    ○ **D.** a bill from 1776 showing the cost of a British uniform

4. Which of the following is a primary source about the Declaration of Independence?

- ○ **F.** an interview with a professor who studies the Declaration
- ◉ **G.** a textbook about the Declaration of Independence
- ◉ **H.** a letter from Thomas Jefferson about the Declaration of Independence
- ○ **J.** a TV show about how the Declaration of Independence was written

5. Which of the following is a primary source about the Stamp Act?

- ○ **A.** an interview with an expert on the Stamp Act
- ○ **B.** a book about famous laws
- ○ **C.** a review of a new book about the Stamp Act
- ◉ **D.** a speech by a British lawmaker who wrote the Stamp Act

Name _____

Syllabication VCCV and VCV Patterns

Choose the correct way to divide into syllables the underlined word in each sentence. Fill in the circle next to the best answer.

1. The man sprinkled <u>powder</u> on his wig.
    - ○ **A.** powde • r
    - ○ **B.** po • wder
    - ◑ **C.** pow • der
    - ○ **D.** powd • er

2. The <u>lunar</u> eclipse lasted a long time.
    - ◑ **F.** lu • nar
    - ○ **G.** lun • ar
    - ○ **H.** luna • r
    - ○ **J.** l • unar

3. She gave a <u>silent</u> laugh.
    - ○ **A.** sil • ent
    - ◑ **B.** si • lent
    - ○ **C.** sile • nt
    - ○ **D.** s • ilent

4. The dog <u>behaved</u> well during the party.
    - ○ **F.** beha • ved
    - ○ **G.** behav • ed
    - ○ **H.** beh • aved
    - ◑ **J.** be • haved

5. I heard the colonist <u>whisper</u> a warning.
    - ◑ **A.** whis • per
    - ○ **B.** whisp • er
    - ○ **C.** wh • isper
    - ○ **D.** whi • sper

STOP

Name _____

Spelling VCCV and VCV Patterns

Find the correctly spelled word to complete each sentence. Fill in the circle beside your answer.

1. Daniel made a _____ trip to the crossroads.

- ○ **A.** rappid
- ◐ **B.** rapid
- ○ **C.** rapud
- ○ **D.** rapped

2. He wondered if the patriots would ever _____.

- ○ **F.** arive
- ○ **G.** errive
- ◐ **H.** arrive
- ○ **J.** uhrive

3. _____ they had decided not to come.

- ○ **A.** Purhaps
- ○ **B.** Perrhaps
- ○ **C.** Purrhaps
- ◐ **D.** Perhaps

4. Daniel became _____ of some voices in the distance.

- ○ **F.** uhware
- ◐ **G.** aware
- ○ **H.** awware
- ○ **J.** eware

5. The patriots finally appeared, ready to _____ the latest news.

- ◐ **A.** collect
- ○ **B.** cullect
- ○ **C.** cuhlect
- ○ **D.** colect

STOP

Name _____

Vocabulary Dictionary: Pronunciation Key

Use the chart to answer the questions. Fill in the circle next to the best answer.

Sound	Spellings	Sample Words
/yōo/	u_e, u, ew, ue	cube, music, few, cue
/ŭ/	u, o, o_e, ou, oe, oo, u_e	duck, son, some, double, does, blood, judge
/ĕ/	e, ea, a	press, bread, any
/ē/	e, ea, ee, i	be, bead, need, piano

1. Which of these could be a sample word for the sound /ŭ/?
   - ○ **A.** hoop
   - ○ **C.** road
   - ○ **B.** pond
   - ◐ **D.** skunk

2. Which of these could be a sample word for the sound /yōo/?
   - ○ **F.** large
   - ○ **H.** ramp
   - ◐ **G.** fume
   - ○ **J.** skit

3. Which of these letter pairs can stand for both the /yōo/ sound and the /ŭ/ sound?
   - ○ **A.** ou
   - ○ **C.** ue
   - ○ **B.** oe
   - ◐ **D.** u_e

4. Which of these could be a sample word for the sound /ĕ/?
   - ◐ **F.** sled
   - ○ **H.** bead
   - ○ **G.** dream
   - ○ **J.** sheet

5. Which of these letters or letter pairs can stand for both the /ĕ/ sound and the /ē/ sound?
   - ○ **A.** a
   - ◐ **C.** ea
   - ○ **B.** i
   - ○ **D.** ee

STOP

Grammar Verb Phrases with *have*

Choose the sentence that is written correctly. Fill in the circle next to the best answer.

1. ○ **A.** The colonists has practiced firing their muskets.
   ◉ **B.** They have loaded the carts with supplies.
   ○ **C.** Their leader have asked two people to ride ahead.
   ○ **D.** I has hoped I could go.

2. ○ **F.** Father have left to join the army before I woke.
   ○ **G.** I has wanted to tell him goodbye.
   ◉ **H.** Mother said he had tried to wake me up.
   ○ **J.** She have walked to the road with him.

3. ◉ **A.** My big brother has attended the secret patriot meetings.
   ○ **B.** The patriots has made plans to form an army.
   ○ **C.** It have been a scary time in Boston.
   ○ **D.** I has hoped it would never lead to war.

4. ○ **F.** Uncle Seth have been hurt in the battle at Lexington.
   ◉ **G.** His friends have brought him home.
   ○ **H.** He have wanted to continue farming after the war.
   ○ **J.** Now his children has planned to farm for him.

5. ○ **A.** We has cooked a big supper this evening.
   ○ **B.** Father have returned from the war.
   ◉ **C.** Our family has come together once again to give thanks.
   ○ **D.** Grandpa have cooked a turkey for the feast.

Grammar *teach/learn, let/leave, sit/set, can/may*

Choose the sentence that is written correctly. Fill in the circle next to the best answer.

1. ○ **A.** Tom Able's mother does not leave him fight in the army.
   ○ **B.** Instead, she learn him how to take care of the farm.
   ◉ **C.** He set a sack of feed in the barn.
   ○ **D.** Then he set on a stool to milk the cow.

2. ○ **F.** "Can I go to the Town Hall meeting?" asked Abigail.
   ○ **G.** "I cannot leave you go until later," said Mr. Brown.
   ○ **H.** "I need you to set by Ana's bed until she wakes," he explained.
   ◉ **J.** "May she come with me?" asked Abigail excitedly.

3. ◉ **A.** "Teach me to sew, Mother," said Emma.
   ○ **B.** "I will learn you tomorrow," Mother said.
   ○ **C.** Mother will leave Emma practice on a patriot uniform.
   ○ **D.** She can sew as she sets near a sunny window.

4. ○ **F.** Please leave Johnny come with me.
   ○ **G.** I can learn him to chop firewood.
   ○ **H.** We will sit the logs on the wagon to haul them home.
   ◉ **J.** Then we can have a fire during the meeting.

5. ○ **A.** Leave us go to the patriots' meeting today.
   ◉ **B.** We will sit on the wooden benches in back.
   ○ **C.** Mother said we can go if we are quiet.
   ○ **D.** Elizabeth will learn us about what it all means.

Name _____

Writing Skills Capitalizing Names of People and Places

Find the sentence that is correct. Fill in the circle next to your answer.

1. ○ **A.** John Hancock was the first person to sign the Declaration of Independence in philadelphia, Pennsylvania.

 ○ **B.** John Hancock was the first person to sign the Declaration of Independence in Philadelphia, Pennsylvania.

 ○ **C.** John hancock was the first person to sign the Declaration of Independence in Philadelphia, pennsylvania.

 ○ **D.** John hancock was the first person to sign the Declaration of Independence in philadelphia, Pennsylvania.

2. ○ **F.** Soldiers from new Hampshire arrived to help Colonel William prescott.

 ○ **G.** Soldiers from New Hampshire arrived to help Colonel william Prescott.

 ○ **H.** Soldiers from New Hampshire arrived to help Colonel William Prescott.

 ○ **J.** Soldiers from new hampshire arrived to help Colonel William Prescott.

3. ○ **A.** George Washington and his army crossed the Delaware River to surprise the British soldiers.

 ○ **B.** George washington and his army crossed the Delaware River to surprise the British soldiers.

 ○ **C.** George Washington and his army crossed the delaware river to surprise the British soldiers.

 ○ **D.** George Washington and his army crossed the Delaware River to surprise the british soldiers.

Go on

4. ○ **F.** Deborah Sampson of plympton, Massachusetts, disguised herself as a man and fought in the Revolutionary War for three years.

○ **G.** Deborah sampson of Plympton, Massachusetts, disguised herself as a man and fought in the Revolutionary War for three years.

◉ **H.** Deborah Sampson of Plympton, Massachusetts, disguised herself as a man and fought in the Revolutionary War for three years.

○ **J.** Deborah Sampson of Plympton, massachusetts, disguised herself as a man and fought in the Revolutionary War for three years.

5. ○ **A.** The Revolutionary War ended on October 19, 1781, when Charles cornwallis surrendered to George Washington at Yorktown, Virginia.

○ **B.** The Revolutionary War ended on October 19, 1781, when charles Cornwallis surrendered to george washington at Yorktown, Virginia.

○ **C.** The Revolutionary War ended on October 19, 1781, when Charles Cornwallis surrendered to George Washington at yorktown, virginia.

◉ **D.** The Revolutionary War ended on October 19, 1781, when Charles Cornwallis surrendered to George Washington at Yorktown, Virginia.

Voices of the Revolution

Level 5, Theme 3: Week 3

Weekly Skills Test Record

Student _____   Date _____

Student Record Form	Possible Score	Criterion Score	Student Score
A: Following Directions	5	4	
B: Prefixes *sub-* and *sur-*	5	4	
C: Spelling Spell Final /l/ or /əl/	5	4	
D: Vocabulary Antonyms	5	4	
E: Grammar Kinds of Adjectives	5	4	
F: Grammar Proper Adjectives	5	4	
TOTAL	30	24	
Total Student Score x 3.33 =			%

Following Directions

Read the passage. Then read each question and fill in the circle next to the best answer.

Make a Kite

You probably know that Benjamin Franklin once flew a kite in a thunderstorm. He did this because he had a hunch that the lightning he saw during the storms was electricity. When he received a shock from a key that he had placed on the string, he knew he was right. Now follow these steps to make a kite of your own.

- First, find two sticks. One of the sticks should be about eight inches shorter than the other one.
- Place the two sticks on top of one another in a cross shape. Tie a piece of string in a knot at the place where the two sticks meet.
- With an adult's help, cut a small notch into both ends of each stick.
- Slide one piece of string through all four notches. Pull the string tight and knot the ends together. Now you've made the kite's frame.
- Place the frame onto a large piece of paper. Cut the paper about half an inch away from the frame all the way around.
- Glue around the edge of the paper, and fold it over so that it covers the string and sticks to the paper inside the frame. Now you've covered the kite's frame.
- Cut a long piece of string that equals the length of the short and longer sticks together.
- Tie one end of the string around the top point of the kite. Make a loop one third of the way down the top stick. (Later, you will tie the kite's tail to this loop.) Tie the other end of the string to the bottom of the kite. Cut off any extra string. You've just made the bridle.
- Measure a piece of string that is at least five times as long as the kite. Tie this string, called the kite line, to the loop that you made in the last step.
- Attach ribbon or crepe paper to make the tail of the kite.
- Now the kite is ready to go!

1. What is the first step in making the kite?
   - ○ **A.** Make a cross shape with the two sticks.
   - ○ **B.** Cover the kite frame with paper.
   - ○ **C.** Find two sticks.
   - ○ **D.** Tie ribbon or crepe paper to make the tail.

2. What is the difference in length between the two sticks?
   - ○ **F.** about eight inches
   - ○ **G.** about half an inch
   - ○ **H.** about five inches
   - ○ **J.** about two inches

3. What should you use to attach the paper to the frame?
   - ○ **A.** string
   - ○ **B.** tape
   - ○ **C.** ribbon or crepe paper
   - ○ **D.** glue

4. Where should an adult make the kite's notches?
   - ○ **F.** around the edges of the paper
   - ○ **G.** at the ends of both sticks
   - ○ **H.** at the knot in the middle
   - ○ **J.** about one-third of the way down the sticks

5. Which of these steps comes directly after making the frame?
   - ○ **A.** making the bridle
   - ○ **B.** making the tail
   - ○ **C.** covering the kite
   - ○ **D.** flying the kite

Name _____

Prefixes *sub-* and *sur-*

Choose the correct meaning for each underlined word. Fill in the circle next to the best answer.

1. Brad's <u>subcompact</u> car fit easily into the parking space.
   - ○ **A.** smaller than a compact
   - ○ **B.** larger than a truck
   - ○ **C.** equal in size to a compact
   - ○ **D.** smaller than a van

2. He went into the <u>substation</u> to mail the letter.
   - ○ **F.** original station
   - ○ **G.** main station
   - ○ **H.** large station
   - ○ **J.** smaller station

3. Please <u>survey</u> the flood damage and then report to the mayor.
   - ○ **A.** look under
   - ○ **B.** look over
   - ○ **C.** look ahead
   - ○ **D.** look toward

4. The <u>submarine</u> craft traveled slowly around the island.
   - ○ **F.** above the water
   - ○ **G.** near the water
   - ○ **H.** under the water
   - ○ **J.** through the water

5. The problems with the design were too great to <u>surmount</u>.
   - ○ **A.** learn
   - ○ **B.** know about
   - ○ **C.** add to
   - ○ **D.** overcome

STOP

Name _____

Spelling Spell Final /l/ or /əl/

**Find the correctly spelled word to complete each sentence.
Fill in the circle beside your answer.**

1. It seemed as if every _____ patriot in Lexington came to the wedding.
   - ○ **A.** singel
   - ○ **B.** singal
   - ◉ **C.** single
   - ○ **D.** singol

2. The wedding was held in the lower _____ of the family's home.
   - ○ **F.** levol
   - ◉ **G.** level
   - ○ **H.** levil
   - ○ **J.** leval

3. The bride looked as lovely as the _____ in her ring.
   - ○ **A.** jewol
   - ○ **B.** jewil
   - ○ **C.** jewal
   - ◉ **D.** jewel

4. Before the wedding, a patriot outside gave a _____.
   - ○ **F.** whislte
   - ◉ **G.** whistle
   - ○ **H.** whistal
   - ○ **J.** whistel

5. This was a _____ that no British soldiers were around.
   - ◉ **A.** signal
   - ○ **B.** signel
   - ○ **C.** signle
   - ○ **D.** signol

STOP

Name _____

Vocabulary Antonyms

Read each sentence. Choose the word that means the opposite of the underlined word. Fill in the circle next to the best answer.

1. The British soldiers were <u>rude</u> when they entered our house.
   - ○ **A.** mean
   - ○ **C.** generous
   - ○ **B.** rough
   - ◐ **D.** polite

2. They were quite <u>noisy</u> as they searched the house.
   - ○ **F.** chatty
   - ○ **H.** slow
   - ◐ **G.** silent
   - ○ **J.** awkward

3. I felt <u>upset</u> to have soldiers in my home.
   - ○ **A.** worried
   - ◐ **C.** calm
   - ○ **B.** excited
   - ○ **D.** bored

4. They hoped to <u>capture</u> an important patriot leader.
   - ○ **F.** catch
   - ○ **H.** discover
   - ◐ **G.** release
   - ○ **J.** replace

5. When they left, the house was very <u>messy</u>.
   - ◐ **A.** neat
   - ○ **C.** untidy
   - ○ **B.** cluttered
   - ○ **D.** small

Name _____

Grammar Kinds of Adjectives

Choose the sentence that is written correctly. Fill in the circle next to the best answer.

1. ○ **A.** Benjamin Franklin walks down an alleys of Philadelphia.
   ◉ **B.** He walks in front of a carriage.
   ○ **C.** The man such as this needs to be careful.
   ○ **D.** He has a important job to do.

2. ○ **F.** Take care of these paper for John Adams.
   ○ **G.** Put them in this folder across the room.
   ◉ **H.** Then read this book about the colonies.
   ○ **J.** Please do this jobs before you leave.

3. ○ **A.** I saw an patriot speaking in the town square.
   ○ **B.** He is a elder in the town.
   ○ **C.** I have never heard an speech like that one.
   ◉ **D.** He drew a crowd of people to hear his ideas.

4. ○ **F.** That book I am holding is called *Common Sense*.
   ◉ **G.** The author of this book is Thomas Paine.
   ○ **H.** I found it on this shelf over there.
   ○ **J.** This ideas in the book are making people think.

5. ○ **A.** Thomas Jefferson is writing an major document.
   ○ **B.** It will send a urgent message to the British king.
   ◉ **C.** Jefferson is a very skilled writer.
   ○ **D.** An group of patriots will sign the document.

F Name _____

Grammar Proper Adjectives

**Choose the sentence that is written correctly. Fill in the circle
next to the best answer.**

1. ○ **A.** The english settlers faced many hardships.
    ○ **B.** During the french and Indian War, they needed help.
    ◐ **C.** The British king was afraid of losing the colonies.
    ○ **D.** He sent supplies and soldiers to the american continent.

2. ○ **F.** James Forten went to a school for african children.
    ◐ **G.** At fourteen, he signed on to an American ship.
    ○ **H.** Soon his ship was attacked by a british vessel.
    ○ **J.** Forten and his american comrades fought bravely.

3. ◐ **A.** As a free African, Forten had many reasons to be afraid of capture.
    ○ **B.** Forten feared falling victim to the west indian slave trade.
    ○ **C.** He had heard stories of british ships carrying slaves to Barbados.
    ○ **D.** George Washington, leader of the american forces, disagreed with
    this practice.

4. ○ **F.** Many european soldiers fought on both sides during the
    Revolutionary War.
    ○ **G.** George Washington hired a prussian officer named von Steuben
    to train his troops.
    ◐ **H.** Washington also received support from the French army.
    ○ **J.** Washington's opponent was the british general Charles Cornwallis.

5. ○ **A.** The Declaration of Independence is one of the most famous
    documents in the english language.
    ○ **B.** Thomas Jefferson, a brilliant virginian colonist, wrote the Declaration.
    ○ **C.** Jefferson may have borrowed some ideas from french writers.
    ◐ **D.** A committee of colonists signed the document and sent it
    to the British king.

(STOP)

Person to Person

Level 5, Theme 4: Week 1

Weekly Skills Test Record

Student _____ Date _____

Student Record Form	Possible Score	Criterion Score	Student Score
A: Problem Solving and Decision Making	5	4	
B: Information and Study Skills Note Taking	5	4	
C: Syllabication VCCCV Pattern	5	4	
D: Spelling VCCCV Pattern	5	4	
E: Vocabulary Base Words and Inflected Forms	5	4	
F: Grammar Comparing with Adjectives	5	4	
G: Grammar Comparing with *good/bad*	5	4	
TOTAL	35	28	
Total Student Score x 2.86 =			%

Problem Solving and Decision Making

Read the passage. Then read each question and fill in the circle next to the best answer.

The Best Solution

It was the day of the city parks' basketball championship. We were all gathered at the court when Sara, our best free-throw shooter, sat down on a bench and said, "I don't feel very well, Coach."

"What's wrong?"

"My stomach . . . my head . . . I think I'm coming down with the flu."

"It's just nerves," said Alvin, our center. "You'll be fine, Sara."

Coach looked at Sara and shook his head. "No, you definitely look pale," he said.

"Take deep breaths, Sara," said Linda, our small forward. "And say to yourself 'I won't be sick, I won't be sick. . . .'"

Coach shook his head. "Forget it. Sara has to go straight to bed. The only thing we can do is forfeit the game."

"*Forfeit?*" Everyone groaned. "But we've worked so hard!"

"Hey, what about my brother, Casey?" I said. "He shoots free throws from his wheelchair better than I can on two good legs."

"But . . . he's never played with us before," said Linda.

"I've seen him play," said Sara. "He's awesome."

"It might be against the rules," said Wally.

"Does anyone have a better idea?" asked Coach.

Alvin shrugged. "We can't forfeit, that's for sure."

Coach turned to me with a grin. "Doug, go get your brother," he said. "Win or lose, we're fielding a team today."

1. What was the problem faced by the team?

- ○ **A.** Casey was in a wheelchair.
- ◉ **B.** The team's best free-throw shooter was sick.
- ○ **C.** The coach was sick.
- ○ **D.** They had to forfeit the game.

2. Which of these solutions was **not** suggested?

- ○ **F.** Have Casey play instead of Sara.
- ○ **G.** Have Sara take deep breaths.
- ○ **H.** Forfeit the game.
- ◉ **J.** Have Coach play instead of Sara.

3. What solution was chosen?

- ○ **A.** Forfeit the game.
- ◉ **B.** Ask Casey to fill in.
- ○ **C.** Have Sara take deep breaths.
- ○ **D.** Have Sara take some aspirin.

4. Why was the chosen solution the best one?

- ○ **F.** It was Coach's idea.
- ○ **G.** It wasn't against the rules.
- ◉ **H.** Casey was a good basketball player.
- ○ **J.** The best athletes always play through pain.

5. Why weren't the other players' solutions chosen?

- ○ **A.** They weren't fair to Casey.
- ◉ **B.** They weren't fair to Sara.
- ○ **C.** They hurt Coach's feelings.
- ○ **D.** They were against the rules.

Name _____

Information and Study Skills Note Taking

Read the sentences. Decide which sentence you would NOT include in notes about a topic. Fill in the circle next to the best answer.

1. ○ **A.** The Inca lived in South America.
   ◐ **B.** Mr. Johnson doesn't know the names of the Inca rulers.
   ○ **C.** The Inca used irrigation to water their crops.
   ○ **D.** The Inca built a huge network of roads.

2. ○ **F.** Hernando Cortés was born in Spain.
   ○ **G.** Cortés conquered central and southern Mexico for Spain.
   ○ **H.** In 1540, Cortés went back to Spain.
   ◐ **J.** Cortés awoke early every morning.

3. ◐ **A.** The piano in the choir room needs to be tuned.
   ○ **B.** The piano is a keyboard instrument.
   ○ **C.** Hammers inside a piano strike wires to make sound.
   ○ **D.** Sound waves from the wires cause the soundboard to vibrate.

Go on ▷

4. ○ **F.** The Declaration of Independence was written in Philadelphia.

○ **G.** Benjamin Franklin lived and worked in Philadelphia.

◉ **H.** Down the street from Independence Hall is a great ice-cream shop.

○ **J.** The name *Philadelphia* means "brotherly love."

5. ○ **A.** Glass is made from sand, soda, and lime.

○ **B.** Melted glass can be poured into a mold.

○ **C.** Sometimes glass blowers blow glass into shapes with their breath.

◉ **D.** Small children shouldn't drink from glass containers.

Syllabication VCCCV Pattern

Choose the correct way to divide into syllables the underlined word in each sentence. Fill in the circle next to the best answer.

1. He is <u>extracting</u> the nail from the board.
   - ○ **A.** extr • act • ing
   - ⬤ **C.** ex • tract • ing
   - ○ **B.** extra • ct • ing
   - ○ **D.** ext • ract • ing

2. The teacher was quite <u>impressed</u> with the student's skill.
   - ⬤ **F.** im • pressed
   - ○ **H.** impre • ssed
   - ○ **G.** imp • ressed
   - ○ **J.** impr • essed

3. Amy signed a <u>contract</u> when she began working for the company.
   - ○ **A.** cont • ract
   - ○ **C.** contr • act
   - ⬤ **B.** con • tract
   - ○ **D.** co • ntract

4. He was flattered by the <u>compliment</u>.
   - ○ **F.** compl • im • ent
   - ○ **H.** co • mpli • ment
   - ○ **G.** comp • li • ment
   - ⬤ **J.** com • pli • ment

5. Let's not <u>exclude</u> anyone from the game.
   - ⬤ **A.** ex • clude
   - ○ **C.** exclu • de
   - ○ **B.** excl • ude
   - ○ **D.** exc • lude

Name _____

Spelling VCCCV Pattern

Find the correctly spelled word to complete each sentence. Fill in the circle beside your answer.

1. _____ we went to the circus last year, Dad and I decided to go again this year.
   - ○ **A.** Altho
   - ○ **B.** Allthough
   - ◉ **C.** Although
   - ○ **D.** Althou

2. We each made a _____ to take in case we got hungry.
   - ○ **F.** sanwich
   - ○ **G.** sanwhich
   - ○ **H.** sandwitch
   - ◉ **J.** sandwich

3. This year we had to walk _____ than ever from the parking lot.
   - ○ **A.** father
   - ◉ **B.** farther
   - ○ **C.** farthur
   - ○ **D.** farthir

4. I tried not to _____ even though walking made me tired.
   - ◉ **F.** complain
   - ○ **G.** complayn
   - ○ **H.** complane
   - ○ **J.** complaine

5. Before we reached the stands, we could hear the _____ and the shouts from the crowd.
   - ○ **A.** applaws
   - ○ **B.** aplause
   - ○ **C.** applauze
   - ◉ **D.** applause

Name _____

Vocabulary Base Words and Inflected Forms

Read each sentence. Fill in the circle next to the best answer.

1. Under which entry word would you look in the dictionary to find the meaning of *laughed*?

   ○ **A.** laughed   ○ **C.** laughter
   ○ **B.** laughing   ◉ **D.** laugh

2. Under which entry word would you look in the dictionary to find the meaning of *hiding*?

   ○ **F.** hid   ○ **H.** hiding
   ◉ **G.** hide   ○ **J.** hidden

3. Under which entry word would you look in the dictionary to find the meaning of *convincing*?

   ◉ **A.** convince   ○ **C.** convinced
   ○ **B.** convinc   ○ **D.** convincing

4. Under which entry word would you look in the dictionary to find the meaning of *planning*?

   ○ **F.** planned   ○ **H.** plann
   ◉ **G.** plan   ○ **J.** plane

5. Under which entry word would you look in the dictionary to find the meaning of *hurried*?

   ○ **A.** hurrying   ◉ **C.** hurry
   ○ **B.** hurries   ○ **D.** hurrie

Grammar Comparing with Adjectives

Choose the sentence that is written correctly. Fill in the circle next to the best answer.

1. ● **A.** I didn't know that Jason is taller than Ann.
   ○ **B.** I didn't know that Jason is more tall than Ann.
   ○ **C.** I didn't know that Jason is tallest than Ann.
   ○ **D.** I didn't know that Jason is more taller than Ann.

2. ○ **F.** Allen is the stronger boy in our class.
   ○ **G.** Allen is the most strongest boy in our class.
   ● **H.** Allen is the strongest boy in our class.
   ○ **J.** Allen is the more stronger boy in our class.

3. ○ **A.** Kate is oldest than Karly.
   ● **B.** Kate is older than Karly.
   ○ **C.** Kate is most older than Karly.
   ○ **D.** Kate is more old than Karly.

4. ○ **F.** That is the bigger balloon I have ever seen.
   ○ **G.** That is the more bigger balloon I have ever seen.
   ○ **H.** That is the most big balloon I have ever seen.
   ● **J.** That is the biggest balloon I have ever seen.

5. ○ **A.** That clown's costume is more funnier than the first clown's.
   ○ **B.** That clown's costume is funniest than the first clown's.
   ● **C.** That clown's costume is funnier than the first clown's.
   ○ **D.** That clown's costume is most funny than the first clown's.

Grammar Comparing with *good/bad*

Choose the sentence that is written correctly. Fill in the circle next to the best answer.

1. ○ **A.** Riley felt goodest than he had ever felt before.
   ○ **B.** Riley felt gooder than he had ever felt before.
   ◉ **C.** Riley felt better than he had ever felt before.
   ○ **D.** Riley felt best than he had ever felt before.

2. ○ **F.** The worstest song I've ever heard is "London Bridge Is Falling Down."
   ◉ **G.** The worst song I've ever heard is "London Bridge Is Falling Down."
   ○ **H.** The worser song I've ever heard is "London Bridge Is Falling Down."
   ○ **J.** The most worse song I've ever heard is "London Bridge Is Falling Down."

3. ◉ **A.** Aunt Julia is the best person in the whole family to visit.
   ○ **B.** Aunt Julia is the better person in the whole family to visit.
   ○ **C.** Aunt Julia is the goodest person in the whole family to visit.
   ○ **D.** Aunt Julia is the gooder person in the whole family to visit.

4. ○ **F.** Losing a game is worser than postponing a game because of rain.
   ○ **G.** Losing a game is badder than postponing a game because of rain.
   ◉ **H.** Losing a game is worse than postponing a game because of rain.
   ○ **J.** Losing a game is worst than postponing a game because of rain.

5. ○ **A.** Jerome is a best overall player than Ron.
   ○ **B.** Jerome is a gooder overall player than Ron.
   ○ **C.** Jerome is a goodest overall player than Ron.
   ◉ **D.** Jerome is a better overall player than Ron.

Person to Person

Level 5, Theme 4: Week 2

Weekly Skills Test Record

Student _____ Date _____

Student Record Form	Possible Score	Criterion Score	Student Score
A: Noting Details	5	4	
B: Information and Study Skills Paraphrasing and Synthesizing	5	4	
C: Syllabication VV Pattern	5	4	
D: Spelling VV Pattern	5	4	
E: Vocabulary More Multiple-Meaning Words	5	4	
F: Grammar Commas in a Series	5	4	
G: Grammar More Uses for Commas	5	4	
H: Writing Skills Combining Sentences	5	4	
TOTAL	40	32	
	Total Student Score x 2.5 =		%

Noting Details

Read the passage. Then read each question and fill in the circle next to the best answer.

Helping Leila Achieve Her Dream

At the age of three, Leila Josefowicz began taking music lessons. Even though she was very young, she loved to listen to her parents' recordings of classical music. As she listened, she sometimes made up stories to go with the music. She decided at a young age that she wanted to learn to play the violin very well.

Today, Leila is a well-known violinist. She has performed with orchestras from Amsterdam to Dallas. Her love of the music helped her achieve her goal. Yet she could not have achieved her dream without the help of many people.

When Leila was growing up, she practiced the violin about four hours every day. She awakened at six o'clock every morning to practice before school. Then she practiced more before she did her homework after school. She even practiced after dinner. Her father would often stay near her as she worked. This helped her feel his support. He also drove her to Los Angeles twice a week.

In Los Angeles, Leila worked with her teacher, Robert Lipsett. If Leila had difficulty with part of a piece, Mr. Lipsett would help her by showing her how to play it. He was patient with her, and he helped her have a good time at her lessons by making her laugh.

Leila's brother and mother helped her, too. Sometimes Steven, her brother, played tether ball with her. At other times, she would take long walks along the beach at Malibu with her brother, her mother, and the dog, Molly. The walks helped Leila to stay relaxed. They also gave the family members time to joke around and have fun.

Many people admire Leila's talent. She would be the first to say, however, that a person's talent depends on a lot of love and support from others.

Go on ⇨

1. Which detail helps you know that Leila wanted to become a musician even when she was very young?

   ○ **A.** Her father stayed near her while she practiced playing the violin.

   ○ **B.** She took lessons in Los Angeles from Mr. Robert Lipsett.

   ○ **C.** She took long walks on the beach with her mother and brother.

   ◉ **D.** She decided that she wanted to learn to play the violin really well.

2. What detail tells you that Leila is a successful violinist?

   ○ **F.** Leila walked on the beach at Malibu.

   ○ **G.** Leila's brother played tether ball with her.

   ◉ **H.** Leila has played in orchestras around the world.

   ○ **J.** Leila loved listening to classical music at age three.

3. Based on the passage, which of these adults did **not** help Leila achieve her dream?

   ○ **A.** Leila's father

   ○ **B.** Mr. Robert Lipsett

   ◉ **C.** Leila's uncle

   ○ **D.** Leila's mother

4. Which word tells you that Robert Lipsett made learning fun?

   ◉ **F.** laugh

   ○ **G.** patient

   ○ **H.** difficulty

   ○ **J.** time

5. Which detail tells you that Leila was committed to her music?

   ○ **A.** She had a dog named Molly.

   ◉ **B.** She practiced about four hours a day.

   ○ **C.** Her teacher lived in Los Angeles.

   ○ **D.** Her father supported her.

B

Name _____

Information and Study Skills
Paraphrasing and Synthesizing

Read paragraphs A and B. Then answer the questions that follow. Fill in the circle next to the best answer.

A student writing a paper on Alexander Graham Bell found the following information. She found Paragraph A in a book called *Famous Inventors*. She found Paragraph B in a newspaper article.

A. Alexander Graham Bell was born in 1847 in Edinburgh, Scotland. As an adult, he moved to Boston, Massachusetts. Bell worked to help people who could not hear well. This interest led him to invent the telephone in 1876. News of his invention quickly spread throughout the country. Bell set up the first telephone exchange in New Haven, Connecticut. By 1884, long distance connections had been established between Boston, Massachusetts, and New York City.

B. If Alexander Graham Bell were alive today, he would be amazed at how his invention has changed the world. Today, people who have trouble hearing use special telephones to communicate with their friends. People around the world use telephone lines to send instant e-mail messages to one another. The same telephone lines allow people to use the Internet to study, shop, and find information about a wide variety of subjects. Telephone lines allow people to communicate with one another in ways that Alexander Graham Bell would never have dreamed of.

1. Which of these is a paraphrase of the underlined sentences in Paragraph A?
   - ○ **A.** Bell worked to help people who could not hear well; this interest led him to invent the telephone in 1876.
   - ◉ **B.** Bell's invention of the telephone in 1876 resulted from his work with people who could not hear well.
   - ○ **C.** Bell helped people who could not hear well.
   - ○ **D.** Bell invented the telephone in 1876.

2. Which of these sentences paraphrases the last sentence in Paragraph A?

- ○ **F.** Long distance connections were set up.
- ○ **G.** Alexander Graham Bell established connections between Boston and New York City in 1884.
- ◉ **H.** Long distance connections between Boston and New York City were made by 1884.
- ○ **J.** By 1876, long distance connections had been made between Boston and New York.

3. Which of these sentences synthesizes the ideas in both paragraphs?

- ○ **A.** The first long distance connections ever made occurred between Boston and New York City.
- ○ **B.** Alexander Graham Bell changed the course of history.
- ○ **C.** Today, people who have trouble hearing can use special telephones.
- ◉ **D.** Bell's invention of the telephone in 1876 led to today's developments in communications.

4. Which of these sentences paraphrases the most significant events in Bell's life mentioned in Paragraph A?

- ◉ **F.** Bell was born in 1847 and invented the telephone in 1876, which led to long distance connections in 1884.
- ○ **G.** Bell was twenty-nine when he invented the telephone.
- ○ **H.** Bell was thirty-seven when long distance connections could be made by telephone.
- ○ **J.** Bell was born in Scotland and later moved to Massachusetts.

5. Which of these sentences synthesizes an idea in Paragraph B?

- ○ **A.** Without Bell's telephone invention people could not own computers.
- ○ **B.** Bell knew that someday the Internet would be invented and people would be able to communicate with friends and family around the world.
- ◉ **C.** The invention of the telephone has made it possible to communicate long distances, send instant e-mails, and study, shop, and find information on the Internet.
- ○ **D.** Alexander Graham Bell made life more difficult for people.

STOP

Name _____

Syllabication VV Pattern

Choose the correct way to divide into syllables the underlined word in each sentence. Fill in the circle next to the best answer.

1. The <u>audience</u> clapped politely at the end of the concert.
    - ○ **A.** aud • ie • nce
    - ○ **B.** au • dien • ce
    - ○ **C.** aud • ien • ce
    - ◉ **D.** au • di • ence

2. The pilot knew a lot about <u>aviation</u>.
    - ○ **F.** av • ia • tion
    - ◉ **G.** a • vi • a • tion
    - ○ **H.** avia • ti • on
    - ○ **J.** a • via • tion

3. Marty doesn't like to watch movies that have <u>violent</u> scenes.
    - ○ **A.** vio • lent
    - ◉ **B.** vi • o • lent
    - ○ **C.** v • io • lent
    - ○ **D.** viol • ent

4. The <u>librarian</u> helped me with my science report.
    - ○ **F.** li • bra • rian
    - ○ **G.** lib • ra • r • ian
    - ○ **H.** li • bra • ria • n
    - ◉ **J.** li • brar • i • an

5. He conducted a <u>scientific</u> study of alligators.
    - ◉ **A.** sci • en • tif • ic
    - ○ **B.** scie • nt • if • ic
    - ○ **C.** scien • ti • fic
    - ○ **D.** sc • ien • ti • fic

STOP

Name _____

Spelling VV Pattern

Find the correctly spelled word to complete each sentence. Fill in the circle beside your answer.

1. My father and I like to go to the _____ each year.
   - ○ **A.** roadio
   - ● **B.** rodeo
   - ○ **C.** rodio
   - ○ **D.** roadeo

2. We had heard on the _____ that this year the crowds would be bigger than ever, and we could see that it was true.
   - ● **F.** radio
   - ○ **G.** raydio
   - ○ **H.** reidio
   - ○ **J.** radeo

3. By the time we entered the arena, the _____ had been completed and everyone knew who would be in the finals.
   - ○ **A.** trails
   - ○ **B.** tryals
   - ● **C.** trials
   - ○ **D.** triels

4. The bull riders _____ excitement when they walked into the ring.
   - ○ **F.** crated
   - ● **G.** created
   - ○ **H.** criated
   - ○ **J.** creatd

5. The clowns' silly tricks were actually skillful _____ to distract the bulls.
   - ○ **A.** manoovers
   - ○ **B.** manuevers
   - ○ **C.** munuvers
   - ● **D.** maneuvers

Vocabulary More Multiple-Meaning Words

Read the following sentences. Find the definition for the underlined word. Fill in the circle next to the best answer.

1. It is a <u>rule</u> of the soccer club that anyone may play.
    - ○ **A.** to govern
    - ○ **B.** an order by a court of law
    - ○ **C.** to mark with lines
    - ◉ **D.** a statement of what to do

2. After her third <u>foul</u>, the basketball player was taken out of the game.
    - ○ **F.** dirty
    - ○ **G.** tangled up
    - ◉ **H.** an unfair play
    - ○ **J.** rainy or stormy

3. The school <u>board</u> will decide when we have the party.
    - ◉ **A.** a group of people
    - ○ **B.** piece of wood
    - ○ **C.** to cover up
    - ○ **D.** to enter

4. When the bell rings we are to <u>head</u> for the lunchroom.
    - ○ **F.** top of the body
    - ○ **G.** leader or boss
    - ◉ **H.** move toward
    - ○ **J.** in first place

5. Running the marathon will <u>test</u> her dedication.
    - ○ **A.** a series of questions
    - ○ **B.** the worth of something
    - ○ **C.** perform an experiment
    - ◉ **D.** challenge

Name _____

Grammar Commas in a Series

Choose the sentence that is written correctly. Fill in the circle next to the best answer.

1. ○ **A.** Please bring me the scissors, tape, and, chalk.
    ○ **B.** Please bring me the scissors, tape and chalk.
    ◉ **C.** Please bring me the scissors, tape, and chalk.
    ○ **D.** Please bring me the scissors and tape and, chalk.

2. ○ **F.** Instead of clothes, Lucia packed games books her knitting, and snacks in her suitcase.
    ○ **G.** Instead of clothes, Lucia packed games and books and her knitting, snacks in her suitcase.
    ◉ **H.** Instead of clothes, Lucia packed games, books, her knitting, and snacks in her suitcase.
    ○ **J.** Instead of clothes, Lucia packed games, books and her knitting and snacks in her suitcase.

3. ○ **A.** Riley made his bed, and fed the dog, and studied his spelling before leaving for school.
    ◉ **B.** Riley made his bed, fed the dog, and studied his spelling before leaving for school.
    ○ **C.** Riley made his bed fed the dog, and studied his spelling before leaving for school.
    ○ **D.** Riley made his bed, fed the dog and studied his spelling before leaving for school.

4. ○ **F.** Lyn packed her lunch with a sandwich crackers, fruit, and carrots.
   ○ **G.** Lyn packed her lunch with a sandwich, crackers fruit, and carrots.
   ○ **H.** Lyn packed her lunch with, a sandwich, crackers, fruit, and carrots.
   ◐ **J.** Lyn packed her lunch with a sandwich, crackers, fruit, and carrots.

5. ○ **A.** Jada brushed her cat gave it a bath, cleaned its ears and dried it with a towel.
   ○ **B.** Jada brushed, her cat gave it a bath, cleaned its ears, and dried it with a towel.
   ○ **C.** Jada brushed her cat, gave it a bath, cleaned its ears, and dried it with a towel.
   ○ **D.** Jada brushed her cat, gave it a bath cleaned its ears and dried it with a towel.

Name _____

Grammar More Uses for Commas

Choose the sentence that is written correctly. Fill in the circle next to the best answer.

1. ○ **A.** What movie Jason, are your parents taking you to see?
    ○ **B.** What movie Jason are your parents, taking you to see?
    ○ **C.** What movie, Jason are your parents taking you to see?
    ◐ **D.** What movie, Jason, are your parents taking you to see?

2. ◐ **F.** Well, I'm not sure of the title.
    ○ **G.** Well I'm not sure, of the title.
    ○ **H.** Well, I'm not sure, of the title.
    ○ **J.** Well I'm not, sure of the title.

3. ○ **A.** Olivia, have you seen the movie, showing at the art museum?
    ◐ **B.** Olivia, have you seen the movie showing at the art museum?
    ○ **C.** Olivia have you seen the movie, showing at the art museum?
    ○ **D.** Olivia, have you, seen the movie showing at the art museum?

4. ○ **F.** Yes, it's an old, black-and-white movie.
    ○ **G.** Yes it's an old, black-and-white movie.
    ◐ **H.** Yes, it's an old black-and-white movie.
    ○ **J.** Yes, it's an old black-and-white, movie.

5. ○ **A.** No but it got, good reviews.
    ◐ **B.** No, but it got good reviews.
    ○ **C.** No but it got good reviews.
    ○ **D.** No, but, it got good reviews.

Writing Skills Combining Sentences

Read the passage. Then read each question and fill in the circle next to the best answer.

¹The family began to prepare for their trip to the beach. ²It was early in the morning. ³Dad made potato salad and sandwiches. ⁴He was in the kitchen.

⁵Mom found the ice chest. ⁶It was in the garage. ⁷Gloria packed the beach towels. ⁸She was in the den.

⁹Gloria put the swim suits in the trunk. ¹⁰She did this right before they left.

1. Which of these shows the best way to combine sentences 1 and 2?
- **A.** Early in the morning, the family began to prepare for their trip to the beach.
- **B.** The family began to prepare, early in the morning, for their trip to the beach.
- **C.** The family began to prepare for their trip to the beach, early in the morning.
- **D.** Early the family began to prepare for their trip to the beach in the morning.

2. Which of these shows the best way to combine sentences 3 and 4?
- **F.** Dad made potato salad and sandwiches, and he was in the kitchen.
- **G.** Dad made potato salad and sandwiches, when he was in the kitchen.
- **H.** Dad made potato salad in the kitchen and sandwiches in the kitchen.
- **J.** In the kitchen, Dad made potato salad and sandwiches.

Go on

3. Which of these shows the best way to combine sentences 5 and 6?

- ○ **A.** Mom found in the garage the ice chest.
- ○ **B.** Mom in the garage found the ice chest.
- ◉ **C.** Mom found the ice chest in the garage.
- ○ **D.** Mom found the ice chest, and it was in the garage.

4. Which of these shows the best way to combine sentences 7 and 8?

- ◉ **F.** In the den, Gloria packed the beach towels.
- ○ **G.** Gloria packed the beach towels, and she was in the den.
- ○ **H.** Gloria packed, in the den, the beach towels.
- ○ **J.** Gloria in the den packed the beach towels.

5. Which of these shows the best way to combine sentences 9 and 10?

- ○ **A.** Gloria put the swim suits, right before they left, in the trunk.
- ◉ **B.** Right before they left, Gloria put the swim suits in the trunk.
- ○ **C.** Gloria put, right before they left, the swim suits in the trunk.
- ○ **D.** They left right before Gloria put the swim suits in the trunk.

Person to Person

Level 5, Theme 4: Week 3

Weekly Skills Test Record

Student _____ Date _____

Student Record Form	Possible Score	Criterion Score	Student Score
A: Compare and Contrast	5	4	
B: Words Ending in -ed or -ing	5	4	
C: Spelling Words Ending in -ed or -ing	5	4	
D: Vocabulary Dictionary: Prefixes	5	4	
E: Grammar Interjections	5	4	
F: Grammar Quotations	5	4	
TOTAL	30	24	
Total Student Score x 3.33 =			%

Compare and Contrast

Read the passage. Then read each question and fill in the circle next to the best answer.

Elena's Two Homes

My name is Elena Fuentes. For most of the year, I live with my mother in San Antonio, Texas. During the summers, we live in Monterrey, Mexico, with my grandmother. I moved to Texas from Monterrey only two years ago, so I feel that Mexico is my real home. In San Antonio, I live in a small apartment. In Mexico, my grandmother's house is very big. My favorite room there is the huge kitchen. I can look at the beautiful view of the mountains from the kitchen window and smell the fragrant dishes that are always cooking on the large stove.

Like my grandmother, my mother loves to cook. However, she works all day when we are in San Antonio. At the end of the day, we usually prepare something quick and easy in our tiny kitchen. On the weekends, we sometimes make flan, a rich custard. My grandmother and I both prefer flan to any other dish.

I think that the hardest part of living in a new country is learning to speak the language. Luckily, my teacher and friends help me learn new words every day. Luckily, too, I have a few close friends in San Antonio. Since we live in different neighborhoods, we ride the bus to school. I do miss my friends in Mexico very much, though. There, I had many friends, and we walked to school together every day.

When I'm in San Antonio, I also miss having pets to play with. I love to play with the pets at my grandmother's house. I throw sticks for Pedrito, her dog, and stroke Gato's soft fur. Gato is a yellow cat that loves to lick the flan from my fingers. We're not allowed to keep pets in our apartment. My mother says that when we move to a house, I can have a kitten. I can't wait!

1. How is Elena's kitchen in San Antonio different from her grandmother's kitchen?
   - ○ **A.** It is filled with wonderful smells.
   - ○ **B.** It has a large stove.
   - ○ **C.** It has a view of the mountains.
   - ◉ **D.** It is very small.

2. How are Elena and her grandmother alike?
   - ◉ **F.** They both love flan.
   - ○ **G.** They both speak English well.
   - ○ **H.** They both live in San Antonio for part of the year.
   - ○ **J.** They both live in Monterrey all year.

3. How do Elena's friendships in Mexico differ from her friendships in San Antonio?
   - ○ **A.** She has fewer friends in San Antonio, and they walk to school with her.
   - ○ **B.** She had more friends in Mexico, and they lived in different neighborhoods.
   - ○ **C.** She had fewer friends in Mexico, and they all lived on the same street.
   - ◉ **D.** She had more friends in Mexico, and they walked to school with her.

4. How are Elena's grandmother and mother alike?
   - ○ **F.** They both visit Monterrey every summer.
   - ◉ **G.** They both love to cook.
   - ○ **H.** They both like to walk to school with Elena.
   - ○ **J.** They both have a dog and a cat.

5. Which of these is a reason that Elena likes being in Mexico better than being in San Antonio?
   - ○ **A.** In San Antonio, she lives in a large house.
   - ○ **B.** In Mexico, she can fix quick and easy meals.
   - ◉ **C.** In Mexico, she can play with her grandmother's pets.
   - ○ **D.** In San Antonio, she has a view of the mountains.

STOP

Words Ending in *-ed* or *-ing*

Read each sentence. Then fill in the circle next to the word that best completes each sentence.

1. Jana was _____ about her birthday gift.
   - ● **A.** bragging
   - ○ **B.** brags
   - ○ **C.** bragged
   - ○ **D.** brag

2. Lily had _____ a large glass of orange juice.
   - ○ **F.** orders
   - ○ **G.** order
   - ● **H.** ordered
   - ○ **J.** ordering

3. Jamal doesn't find clowns very _____.
   - ○ **A.** amuse
   - ● **B.** amusing
   - ○ **C.** amuses
   - ○ **D.** amused

4. They _____ special invitations last night.
   - ○ **F.** decorating
   - ● **G.** decorated
   - ○ **H.** decorates
   - ○ **J.** decorate

5. Yesterday, she _____ to help him with his science homework.
   - ● **A.** offered
   - ○ **B.** offer
   - ○ **C.** offering
   - ○ **D.** offers

Name _____

Spelling Words Ending in *-ed* or *-ing*

Find the correctly spelled word to complete each sentence. Fill in the circle beside your answer.

1. This year, for the rodeo, we _____ to wear cowboy hats.
   - ○ **A.** decuded
   - ◉ **B.** decided
   - ○ **C.** diecided
   - ○ **D.** deacided

2. We _____ to watch the bull riding event first.
   - ○ **F.** planed
   - ○ **G.** plaaned
   - ◉ **H.** planned
   - ○ **J.** plannd

3. The first rider fell off, _____ in the clowns coming out to help.
   - ◉ **A.** resulting
   - ○ **B.** reasulting
   - ○ **C.** reesulting
   - ○ **D.** resalting

4. Their _____ tricks kept people laughing.
   - ○ **F.** amuzing
   - ◉ **G.** amusing
   - ○ **H.** amewsing
   - ○ **J.** ahmusing

5. Their tricks kept the rider _____ from the angry bull.
   - ○ **A.** sheltred
   - ○ **B.** shealtered
   - ○ **C.** sheltirred
   - ◉ **D.** sheltered

STOP

Name _____

Vocabulary Dictionary: Prefixes

Read the dictionary entries in the chart. Find the definition for the underlined word. Fill in the circle next to the best answer.

> **in-** A prefix that means "not."
> **com-** A prefix that means "together" or "with."
> **re-** A prefix that means "again" or "back."

1. His answer to the math question was <u>incorrect</u>.
   - ○ **A.** not right
   - ○ **B.** better
   - ○ **C.** almost right
   - ○ **D.** a good effort

2. The machine <u>compressed</u> the sheets of cardboard into small stacks.
   - ○ **F.** pushed away
   - ○ **G.** found a difference
   - ○ **H.** separated into two parts
   - ○ **J.** squeezed together

3. Before I knew it, my friend <u>reappeared</u> in the doorway.
   - ○ **A.** leaned against
   - ○ **B.** stood
   - ○ **C.** came into view again
   - ○ **D.** walked through

4. The collie will <u>return</u> to her doghouse.
   - ○ **F.** turn around
   - ○ **G.** run away from
   - ○ **H.** go back to
   - ○ **J.** put back

5. When John's leg was in a cast he was <u>inactive</u>.
   - ○ **A.** nervous
   - ○ **B.** not active
   - ○ **C.** busy
   - ○ **D.** not paying attention

Name _____

Grammar Interjections

Choose the sentence that is written correctly. Fill in the circle next to the best answer.

1. ◯ **A.** Oh! I've spilled juice on my shirt.
   ◯ **B.** Oh I've spilled juice on my shirt.
   ◯ **C.** Oh! I've spill juice on my shirt.
   ◯ **D.** Oh I've spilled juice, on my shirt.

2. ◯ **F.** Ouch,! I stepped on a rock in the playground.
   ◯ **G.** Ouch, I stepped on a rock, in the playground.
   ◉ **H.** Ouch! I stepped on a rock in the playground.
   ◯ **J.** Ouch I stepped on a rock in the playground.

3. ◯ **A.** Uh oh! Joshua almost ran into, the door frame.
   ◯ **B.** Uh oh? Joshua, almost ran into the door frame.
   ◯ **C.** Uh oh Joshua almost ran into the door frame.
   ◉ **D.** Uh oh! Joshua almost ran into the door frame.

4. ◯ **F.** That glass door isn't open wait!
   ◉ **G.** That glass door isn't open. Wait!
   ◯ **H.** That glass door, isn't open! Wait?
   ◯ **J.** That glass! door isn't open. wait!

5. ◉ **A.** Look, that flock of egrets is flying back north.
   ◯ **B.** Look, that flock of egrets, is flying back north.
   ◯ **C.** Look! that flock of egrets is flying back north.
   ◯ **D.** Look, that flock, of egrets is flying back north!

Grammar Quotations

Choose the sentence that is written correctly. Fill in the circle next to the best answer.

1. ○ **A.** Tony said, "I hear a growling noise over toward that corner,"
   ○ **B.** "Tony said, I hear a growling noise over toward that corner."
   ◉ **C.** Tony said, "I hear a growling noise over toward that corner."
   ○ **D.** Tony said. "I hear a growling noise over toward that corner."

2. ◉ **F.** "Don't you just hate being scared?" asked Marti.
   ○ **G.** Don't you just hate being scared. asked Marti.
   ○ **H.** "Don't you just hate being scared? asked Marti.
   ○ **J.** Don't you just hate being scared, asked Marti."

3. ○ **A.** I think we should see what's making that noise," replied Ty.
   ○ **B.** "I think we should see what's making that noise." replied Ty.
   ○ **C.** "I think we should see what's making that noise, replied Ty.
   ◉ **D.** "I think we should see what's making that noise," replied Ty.

4. ○ **F.** "I don't want to I think we should just leave," answered Marti.
   ◉ **G.** "I don't want to. I think we should just leave," answered Marti.
   ○ **H.** "I don't want to i think we should just leave," answered Marti.
   ○ **J.** "I don't want to. I think we should just leave." answered Marti.

5. ○ **A.** Tony laughed, "it's only a group of puppies. They're fighting over a toy."
   ◉ **B.** Tony laughed, "It's only a group of puppies. They're fighting over a toy."
   ○ **C.** Tony laughed, "It's only a group of puppies." "They're fighting over a toy."
   ○ **D.** Tony laughed! "It's only a group of puppies. They're fighting over a toy."

STOP

Person to Person

Level 5, Theme 4: Week 4

Weekly Skills Test Record

Student _____   Date _____

Student Record Form	Possible Score	Criterion Score	Student Score
A: Making Inferences	5	4	
B: Suffixes -ly, -ness, -ment, -ful, -less	5	4	
C: Spelling Suffixes -ly, -ness, -ment, -ful, -less	5	4	
D: Vocabulary Word Connotations	5	4	
E: Grammar Abbreviations	5	4	
F: Grammar Titles	5	4	
TOTAL	30	24	
Total Student Score x 3.33 =			%

Making Inferences

Read the passage. Then read each question and fill in the circle next to the best answer.

The Reason Why

"How about a snack?" Kim asked Alicia. Alicia, a new girl at school, had come home with Kim. Earlier that week Alicia had told Kim how difficult it was to be a new student at a school. Kim wanted to make Alicia feel welcome. She even hoped that she and Alicia would become close friends.

A few minutes later, Kim's older brother walked into the kitchen carrying a tennis racket. "Hi, I'm Lee," he said. Alicia's face lit up when she saw Lee. Soon the two were talking excitedly about tennis while Kim fixed sandwiches. As they ate, Alicia and Lee continued talking. It seemed to Kim that Alicia had completely forgotten about her.

When they finished eating, Kim suggested that she and Alicia go outside to play with Petunia, the family's dog. Lee followed, suggesting that they throw tennis balls to Petunia.

Later, after Alicia had gone home, Kim began to pout. She said, "Thanks a lot, Lee. I think you and Alicia were both rude. Now, whenever she comes over, she'll be coming to see you, not me."

Lee was surprised at his sister's outburst. They rarely had disagreements. He didn't even know what he had done wrong. He thought he had simply been a good host to Kim's friend.

Although Kim's feelings were still hurt, she greeted Alicia with a smile the next day at school. Alicia told Kim that she had enjoyed her visit. "I'm so glad that I got to meet Lee," she said. "I have a brother his age." Then her face fell. "I don't get to see him very often, though. He goes to college in another state. It's so lonely without him."

Kim immediately understood that Alicia had not been rude at all. "We loved having you visit us," she replied. "Why don't you call your mother and ask her if you can come again today?"

Go on

1. How do you know that Alicia's family has probably moved recently?
   - ○ **A.** She talks about moving to a new house.
   - ◉ **B.** She tells Kim how difficult it is to be a new girl in school.
   - ○ **C.** She says she has not yet finished unpacking.
   - ○ **D.** She talks about how her brother moved away.

2. Why does Alicia's face light up when she sees Lee?
   - ○ **F.** Lee is in one of Alicia's classes.
   - ○ **G.** Alicia has another friend named Lee.
   - ◉ **H.** Lee reminds Alicia of her brother.
   - ○ **J.** Lee reminds Alicia of her best friend.

3. Which of these does Alicia most likely do as a hobby?
   - ◉ **A.** She plays tennis.
   - ○ **B.** She makes different kinds of snacks.
   - ○ **C.** She runs track.
   - ○ **D.** She takes a course at the local college.

4. Why does Kim pout when Alicia leaves?
   - ◉ **F.** She is angry that Lee talked to Alicia so much.
   - ○ **G.** She worries that Alicia didn't like her dog.
   - ○ **H.** She doesn't want to talk about tennis.
   - ○ **J.** Lee didn't help her fix the snack.

5. How does Kim most likely feel at the end of the story?
   - ○ **A.** She is angry at Lee and Alicia.
   - ◉ **B.** She feels relieved to know why Alicia talked to Lee.
   - ○ **C.** She resents that Alicia has a brother, too.
   - ○ **D.** She is excited that Lee will be at home that afternoon.

Suffixes *-ly, -ness, -ment, -ful, -less*

Choose the correct meaning for each underlined word. Fill in the circle next to the best answer.

1. My best friend <u>eagerly</u> accepted her award for helping young children.
   - ● **A.** in an eager way
   - ○ **B.** lacking eagerness
   - ○ **C.** wanting to be eager
   - ○ **D.** able to be eager

2. The <u>happiness</u> she felt showed on her face.
   - ○ **F.** wanting to be happy
   - ○ **G.** not being happy
   - ○ **H.** having the power to be happy
   - ● **J.** the condition of being happy

3. In her <u>excitement</u>, she did not see the edge of the stage.
   - ○ **A.** able to be excited
   - ○ **B.** not being excited
   - ● **C.** the condition of being excited
   - ○ **D.** wanting to be excited

4. I was <u>fearful</u> that she might fall down.
   - ○ **F.** without fear
   - ● **G.** full of fear
   - ○ **H.** able to have fear
   - ○ **J.** using fear

5. The boy was <u>speechless</u> after he received his award.
   - ● **A.** without speech
   - ○ **B.** full of speech
   - ○ **C.** using speech
   - ○ **D.** able to have speech

Name _____

Spelling Suffixes *-ly, -ness, -ment, -ful, -less*

Find the correctly spelled word to complete each sentence.
Fill in the circle beside your answer.

1. Rodeo clowns save _____ lives every year.
   - ○ **A.** countles
   - ◉ **C.** countless
   - ○ **B.** cauntless
   - ○ **D.** kountless

2. Their _____ also keeps many riders from being hurt.
   - ○ **F.** helpfullness
   - ○ **H.** helpfulnes
   - ◉ **G.** helpfulness
   - ○ **J.** helpfuelnes

3. They seem to get _____ out of playing tricks.
   - ◉ **A.** enjoyment
   - ○ **C.** enjoymint
   - ○ **B.** unjoyment
   - ○ **D.** enjoymunt

4. Their job is to see that fallen riders get out of the ring _____.
   - ○ **F.** saffly
   - ○ **H.** saftly
   - ○ **G.** saffely
   - ◉ **J.** safely

5. The clowns may act silly, but they keep a _____ eye on the angry bulls.
   - ○ **A.** watchfull
   - ◉ **C.** watchful
   - ○ **B.** wachful
   - ○ **D.** washful

Name _____

Vocabulary Word Connotations

Read each sentence. Fill in the circle next to the best answer.

1. Complete the sentence with the word that has a positive connotation.

    A _____ breeze blew through the town.
    - ○ **A.** frigid
    - ◉ **B.** cool
    - ○ **C.** wintry
    - ○ **D.** chilly

2. Complete the sentence with the word that has a negative connotation.
    We worked all day under the _____ sun.
    - ○ **F.** bright
    - ○ **G.** glowing
    - ○ **H.** shining
    - ◉ **J.** scorching

3. Complete the sentence with the word that has a positive connotation.
    Clouds made the afternoon light seem _____.
    - ○ **A.** murky
    - ○ **B.** dreary
    - ◉ **C.** soft
    - ○ **D.** gloomy

4. Complete the sentence with the word that has a negative connotation.
    To find out the truth, the attorney had to _____ the witnesses a second time.
    - ○ **F.** question
    - ○ **G.** interview
    - ○ **H.** ask
    - ◉ **J.** bully

5. Complete the sentence with the word that has a positive connotation.
    For vacation, our family rented a small _____ in the woods.
    - ○ **A.** shack
    - ◉ **B.** cottage
    - ○ **C.** hut
    - ○ **D.** shed

Grammar Abbreviations

Choose the sentence that is written correctly. Fill in the circle next to the best answer.

1. ○ **A.** The teacher said, "My name is Ms. Alice N Hawes."
   ○ **B.** The teacher said, My name is Ms Alice N Hawes.
   ◉ **C.** The teacher said, "My name is Ms. Alice N. Hawes."
   ○ **D.** The teacher said, "My name is Ms Alice N. Hawes."

2. ○ **F.** Mrs. Murray's address is 16 Pumpkin st., Charlton MA.
   ○ **G.** Mrs. Murray's address is 16 Pumpkin ST. Charlton, MA.
   ○ **H.** Mrs Murray's address is 16 Pumpkin St, Charlton, Ma.
   ◉ **J.** Mrs. Murray's address is 16 Pumpkin St., Charlton, MA.

3. ◉ **A.** A Doctor of Medicine, Dr. Wang signs M.D. after her name.
   ○ **B.** A Doctor of Medicine, Doc. Wang signs M.D. after her name.
   ○ **C.** A Doctor of Medicine, Dctr. Wang signs M.D. after her name.
   ○ **D.** A Doctor of Medicine, Dr Wang signs M.D. after her name.

4. ○ **F.** My dad's full name is Robert P Altman, Jr.
   ◉ **G.** My dad's full name is Robert P. Altman, Jr.
   ○ **H.** My dad's full name is Robert P. Altman, Jnr.
   ○ **J.** My dad's full name is Robert P Altman Junior.

5. ○ **A.** For more information about the product, write to Jones-Wilson, Incorp.
   ◉ **B.** For more information about the product, write to Jones-Wilson, Inc.
   ○ **C.** For more information about the product, write to Jones-Wilson, Incr.
   ○ **D.** For more information about the product, write to Jones-Wilson, Ink.

Grammar Titles

**Choose the sentence that is written correctly. Fill in the circle
next to the best answer.**

1. ○ **A.** The short story "The Tidy Drawer" is shorter than the book "The
   Beach in Winter."

   ◉ **B.** The short story "The Tidy Drawer" is shorter than the book <u>The
   Beach in Winter</u>.

   ○ **C.** The short story <u>The Tidy Drawer</u> is shorter than the book The Beach
   in Winter.

   ○ **D.** The short story the tidy drawer is shorter than the book The Beach in
   Winter.

2. ○ **F.** <u>Three Blind Mice</u> is a song that is not often heard anymore.

   ○ **G.** "three blind mice" is a song that is not often heard anymore.

   ○ **H.** "three Blind Mice" is a song that is not often heard anymore.

   ◉ **J.** "Three Blind Mice" is a song that is not often heard anymore.

3. ◉ **A.** "Last Summer at the Lake" is a short story about a group of school
   friends.

   ○ **B.** "Last summer at the lake" is a short story about a group of school
   friends.

   ○ **C.** <u>Last Summer at the Lake</u> is a short story about a group of school
   friends.

   ○ **D.** "Last Summer At The Lake" is a short story about a group of school
   friends.

4. ○ **F.** The movie I, Robot was based on the short story collection "I, Robot" by Isaac Asimov.

○ **G.** The movie "I, Robot" was based on the short story collection "I, Robot" by Isaac Asimov.

◉ **H.** The movie <u>I, Robot</u> was based on the short story collection <u>I, Robot</u> by Isaac Asimov.

○ **J.** The movie "I, Robot" was based on the short story collection I, Robot by Isaac Asimov.

5. ○ **A.** This week at camp we learned how to sing <u>If You're Happy and You Know It</u>.

◉ **B.** This week at camp we learned how to sing "If You're Happy and You Know It."

○ **C.** This week at camp we learned how to sing "If you're happy and you know it."

○ **D.** This week at camp we learned how to sing If You're Happy and You Know It.

One Land, Many Trails

Level 5, Theme 5: Week 1

Weekly Skills Test Record

Student _____ Date _____

Student Record Form	Possible Score	Criterion Score	Student Score
A: Drawing Conclusions	5	4	
B: Prefixes *un-*, *dis-*, *in-*, *re-*; Suffix *-ion*	5	4	
C: Spelling Prefixes *un-*, *dis-*, *in-*, *re-*; Suffix *-ion*	5	4	
D: Vocabulary Analogies	5	4	
E: Grammar Subject/Object Pronouns	5	4	
F: Grammar Using *I* and *me*	5	4	
TOTAL	30	24	
Total Student Score x 3.33 =			%

Drawing Conclusions

Read the passage. Then read each question and fill in the circle next to the best answer.

The Pony Express

The Pony Express marked one of the most exciting times in the history of the West. Three men formed the business in 1860. They wanted to show the government that they could deliver mail between Missouri and California. They hoped that the government would eventually hire them and their new business would make a lot of money.

The men planned for a relay of riders to carry the mail between the states. They set up stations every five to twenty miles where the riders could change horses. The stations formed a 2000-mile trail. Next, the owners hired riders to carry the mail. To do this, they posted the following ad:

"Wanted. Young, skinny, wiry fellows. Not over 18. Must be expert riders. Willing to risk death daily."

Riders who signed on with the Pony Express had a very tough job. They galloped at full speed from station to station. At each station, they leapt from one horse, mounted another, and raced ahead. When a rider had traveled about seventy-five to one hundred miles, he handed the mail off to a new rider, who continued the journey.

The difficult trip took about ten days in the summer and twelve to sixteen days in the winter. The shortest trip was the delivery of a copy of the speech that Abraham Lincoln gave when he became President. It took only seven days and seventeen hours.

When the Pony Express began, customers paid five dollars to have a letter delivered. Later, however, the price dropped to one dollar. The Pony Express ended in 1861 when the telegraph, which allowed people to send messages by telegram, was invented. Even though the Pony Express did not last very long, its brave, young riders will always be remembered.

1. Why did the owners of the Pony Express set up a relay rather than sending one man at a time?
   - ○ **A.** The relay made the delivery of the mail faster.
   - ○ **B.** The relay made the delivery of the mail more exciting for the riders.
   - ○ **C.** Riders didn't want to face the dangers of the trip alone.
   - ○ **D.** Riders wanted to see other people as they worked.

2. Why did each rider ride more than one horse?
   - ○ **F.** All the horses needed to be exercised.
   - ○ **G.** There were different horses waiting at each station.
   - ○ **H.** Riding more than one horse made the trip more interesting.
   - ○ **J.** The horses became tired after running so hard.

3. How many relay stations were set up?
   - ○ **A.** a few
   - ○ **B.** a dozen
   - ○ **C.** a half-dozen
   - ○ **D.** many

4. Why did the trip take longer in winter?
   - ○ **F.** The riders followed a different trail.
   - ○ **G.** The riders spent a long time at each station.
   - ○ **H.** Bad weather made traveling more difficult.
   - ○ **J.** The horses couldn't run as fast in the winter.

5. Why did the Pony Express end the same year that the telegraph was invented?
   - ○ **A.** Many horses were sick that year.
   - ○ **B.** The telegraph allowed people to send messages more quickly than the Pony Express.
   - ○ **C.** All the Pony Express riders went to work for the telegraph companies.
   - ○ **D.** The owners of the Pony Express sold their business to the telegraph companies.

STOP

Name _____

Prefixes *un-*, *dis-*, *in-*, *re-*; Suffix *-ion*

Choose the correct meaning for each underlined word. Fill in the circle next to the best answer.

1. Charles was <u>unprepared</u> for the test.
   - ◉ **A.** not prepared
   - ○ **B.** well prepared
   - ○ **C.** badly prepared
   - ○ **D.** prepared before

2. Becky <u>disagreed</u> with his decision.
   - ○ **F.** agreed before
   - ◉ **G.** did not agree
   - ○ **H.** partly agreed
   - ○ **J.** mostly agreed

3. The colts were <u>inactive</u> in the cold.
   - ○ **A.** very active
   - ○ **B.** able to be active
   - ○ **C.** more than active
   - ◉ **D.** not active

4. The ranch hands <u>rebuilt</u> the corral.
   - ○ **F.** built before
   - ○ **G.** did not build
   - ◉ **H.** built again
   - ○ **J.** took apart

5. The <u>reflection</u> of the rising sun shone in the lake.
   - ○ **A.** something that is not reflected
   - ◉ **B.** something that is reflected
   - ○ **C.** badly reflected
   - ○ **D.** to reflect

STOP

Name _____

Spelling Prefixes *un-*, *dis-*, *in-*, *re-*; Suffix *-ion*

Find the correctly spelled word to complete each sentence.
Fill in the circle beside your answer.

1. The Mexican soldiers _____ the town from the south.
   - ⦿ **A.** reentered
   - ◯ **B.** reintered
   - ◯ **C.** rentered
   - ◯ **D.** reenterred

2. Some people were _____ of their arrival.
   - ◯ **F.** unawar
   - ◯ **G.** inaware
   - ⦿ **H.** unaware
   - ◯ **J.** unawhare

3. The _____ built as the soldiers rode through the streets.
   - ◯ **A.** tenshun
   - ⦿ **B.** tension
   - ◯ **C.** tenchion
   - ◯ **D.** tinsion

4. The townspeople stayed _____ their homes and businesses.
   - ◯ **F.** enside
   - ◯ **G.** innside
   - ◯ **H.** incide
   - ⦿ **J.** inside

5. They hoped the soldiers would _____ quickly.
   - ◯ **A.** dissapear
   - ⦿ **B.** disappear
   - ◯ **C.** disapere
   - ◯ **D.** disapier

STOP

Vocabulary Analogies

Choose the word that best completes each analogy. Fill in the circle next to the best answer.

1. <u>Potato</u> is to <u>vegetable</u> as <u>piano</u> is to _____.
   - ○ **A.** flute
   - ○ **B.** drum
   - ◉ **C.** instrument
   - ○ **D.** carrot

2. <u>Plentiful</u> is to <u>rare</u> as <u>cramped</u> is to _____.
   - ○ **F.** small
   - ◉ **G.** roomy
   - ○ **H.** many
   - ○ **J.** few

3. <u>Lose</u> is to <u>misplace</u> as <u>locate</u> is to _____.
   - ◉ **A.** find
   - ○ **B.** steal
   - ○ **C.** miss
   - ○ **D.** forget

4. <u>Explorer</u> is to <u>adventurer</u> as <u>teacher</u> is to _____.
   - ○ **F.** follower
   - ○ **G.** student
   - ○ **H.** librarian
   - ◉ **J.** instructor

5. <u>Pen</u> is to <u>write</u> as <u>broom</u> is to _____.
   - ○ **A.** closet
   - ◉ **B.** sweep
   - ○ **C.** handle
   - ○ **D.** straws

E

Name _____

Grammar Subject/Object Pronouns

Choose the sentence that is written correctly. Fill in the circle next to the best answer.

1. ○ **A.** My father watches us move about in our tiny home.
    ○ **B.** Him dreams of living in a bigger house in California.
    ○ **C.** He tells we to pack our belongings.
    ○ **D.** Us are excited about moving to a new place.

2. ○ **F.** Mrs. Jackson teaches I and my classmates at the frontier school.
    ○ **G.** Her is a woman who has taught for many years.
    ◉ **H.** She is in charge of students from first to twelfth grade.
    ○ **J.** Them are not easy to teach.

3. ○ **A.** Ben and me think something has startled the horses.
    ○ **B.** We will go see what is wrong with they.
    ○ **C.** Them are galloping around the corral.
    ◉ **D.** Maybe a wild animal has scared them.

4. ○ **F.** Me see that Mary has brought carrots for the horses.
    ○ **G.** Them will like the carrots.
    ◉ **H.** The horses will calm down for her.
    ○ **J.** Her always knows what to do for the animals.

5. ○ **A.** Ben and me rode horses in the pasture.
    ◉ **B.** We found bobcat paw prints near the pond.
    ○ **C.** Us will have to put the horses in the corral each night.
    ○ **D.** That will keep they safe.

Name _____

Grammar Using *I* and *me*

**Choose the sentence that is written correctly. Fill in the circle
next to the best answer.**

1. ○ **A.** Hannah asked Sarah, Jim, and I to ride in her wagon.
   ○ **B.** "Could you give Bill and I a ride, too?" asked Sal.
   ◉ **C.** "Yes, you can come with me," replied Hannah.
   ○ **D.** Bill, Jim, and me sat in the back of the wagon while the others sat
   up front.

2. ◉ **F.** Bill, Jim, and I talked all the way into town.
   ○ **G.** Me told them about my dog, Maizie.
   ○ **H.** She was given to I as a birthday present last year.
   ○ **J.** Maize likes to play with I, Tom, and Paul.

3. ○ **A.** Hannah, Sarah, and me shopped in the dry goods store.
   ◉ **B.** I bought sacks of flour and sugar.
   ○ **C.** Sarah helped I carry the sacks to the wagon.
   ○ **D.** Then me and Sarah helped load Hannah's purchases into the wagon.

4. ○ **F.** Us sat on top of the sacks on the way home.
   ○ **G.** The ride home was fun for I.
   ○ **H.** Me taught my friends a few new songs.
   ◉ **J.** We practiced the songs until I saw my home in the distance.

5. ◉ **A.** The boys helped me unload my sacks and carry them into the house.
   ○ **B.** Me said goodbye to my friends, and they drove off singing songs.
   ○ **C.** Mother and me smiled as the songs faded in the evening air.
   ○ **D.** It had been a good day for I.

One Land, Many Trails

Level 5, Theme 5: Week 2

Weekly Skills Test Record

Student _____ Date _____

Student Record Form	Possible Score	Criterion Score	Student Score
A: Propaganda	5	4	
B: Information and Study Skills Comparing Information from More Than One Source	5	4	
C: Stressed and Unstressed Syllables	5	4	
D: Spelling Unstressed Syllables	5	4	
E: Vocabulary Dictionary: Suffixes	5	4	
F: Grammar Possessive Pronouns	5	4	
G: Grammar Contractions	5	4	
H: Writing Skills Combining Sentences with Pronouns	5	4	
TOTAL	40	32	
Total Student Score x 2.5 =			%

Name _____

Propaganda

Read the passage. Then read each question and fill in the circle next to the best answer.

Cowboys Needed

Rusty McCall needs cowhands to help him round up and break wild mustangs. If you need some money, this may be the job for you.

"The job is exciting and just plain fun. There's nothing more thrilling than climbing on the back of an untamed mustang," says McCall, known all around the West for his riding skills.

If you want to apply, you must be an expert roper and rider. You must also have experience rounding up horses. All the cowboys who helped during the last roundup had the best time of their lives. They received some of the highest pay in the area.

You will be paid one whole dollar a day. In addition, each cowboy will receive three hot, delicious meals every day. Comfortable housing will be provided in the bunkhouses at the ranch. The bunkhouses hold sixteen men each.

Don't miss out! Cowboys from far and wide will soon be trying to rope this once-in-a-lifetime opportunity. Sign up now so you won't be left in the dust.

1. What is the purpose of this passage?
   - ○ **A.** to describe the life of a cowboy
   - ◐ **B.** to encourage cowboys to work for Rusty McCall
   - ○ **C.** to evaluate the life of a cowboy
   - ○ **D.** to express an opinion about wild mustangs

2. Which statement is an example of overgeneralization?

○ **F.** Rusty McCall needs cowhands to help him round up and break wild mustangs.

○ **G.** If you want to apply, you must be an expert roper and rider.

◉ **H.** All the cowboys who helped during the last roundup had the best time of their lives.

○ **J.** The pay is one whole dollar a day.

3. What form of propaganda is used in the following statement?

"There's nothing more thrilling than climbing on the back of an untamed mustang," says McCall, known around the state for his riding skills.

◉ **A.** testimonial

○ **B.** bandwagon

○ **C.** transfer

○ **D.** faulty cause and effect

4. What form of propaganda is used in the last paragraph of the passage?

◉ **F.** bandwagon

○ **G.** overgeneralization

○ **H.** testimonial

○ **J.** transfer

5. Which of the following statements about the job is most likely to be true?

○ **A.** The bunk beds are comfortable.

○ **B.** The meals are all delicious.

○ **C.** The cowboys will have fun.

◉ **D.** The bunkhouses hold sixteen men each.

Information and Study Skills Comparing Information from More Than One Source

Read paragraphs A, B, C, and D. Then answer the questions that follow. Fill in the circle next to the best answer.

A. From the diary of Annie Stanley, 1850

The early days were the worst. My husband left for work before dawn and mined for gold all day. One day, I decided to open a hotel. I started by serving hot meals to miners at a cost of a dollar a meal. Soon, I had saved enough money to build a hotel with five guest rooms. . . .

B. From *Encyclopedia of the West*

Because he needed lumber for his ranch, James Sutter sent twenty men to the American River to build a sawmill in late 1846. James Marshall was one of these men. At the river, Marshall found a lump of gold the size of a small pea. Soon after, he found another and another. Men with him began to find gold, too. Word of Marshall's discovery spread quickly. By 1848, people along the east coast had heard the news. . . .

C. From *California Times* newspaper, June 7, 2001

Gold Fever: The Story of the 49ers, an exciting exhibition, will open today at the Museum of History. Visitors to the exhibition will view tools used by the miners, paintings showing events that occurred during the period, and photographs of actual events. . . .

D. From *The Real Story About the 49ers*, by Rupert McDonald, director of the *Gold Rush Association*

In my opinion, although the 49ers changed history, they ruined one of the most beautiful regions in our country. . . .

1. Which source provides an eyewitness account?
   - ○ **A.** A
   - ○ **B.** B
   - ○ **C.** C
   - ○ **D.** D

2. Which sources would be most likely to contain biased information?
   - ○ **F.** A and B
   - ○ **G.** B and C
   - ○ **H.** C and D
   - ○ **J.** A and D

3. Which source would be most likely to provide objective details about the daily life of many people during the Gold Rush?
   - ○ **A.** A
   - ○ **B.** B
   - ○ **C.** C
   - ○ **D.** D

4. Which source would be most likely to have accurate information about dates of important events during the Gold Rush?
   - ○ **F.** A
   - ○ **G.** B
   - ○ **H.** C
   - ○ **J.** D

5. What is the author's purpose for writing paragraph **A?**
   - ○ **A.** to describe her experiences
   - ○ **B.** to explain how to mine for gold
   - ○ **C.** to state her opinion about the Gold Rush
   - ○ **D.** to help people learn more about the Gold Rush

Name _____

Stressed and Unstressed Syllables

Choose the word in which the syllables are stressed correctly.
Fill in the circle next to the best answer.

1. She can trace her <u>ancestors</u> back to Greece.
   - ○ **A.** an CES tors
   - ○ **B.** an ces TORS
   - ○ **C.** AN ces TORS
   - ◉ **D.** AN ces tors

2. The little boy could <u>multiply</u> the numbers in his head.
   - ◉ **F.** MUL ti ply
   - ○ **G.** mul TI ply
   - ○ **H.** mul TI PLY
   - ○ **J.** MUL TI ply

3. <u>Agriculture</u> was their only way to make a living.
   - ○ **A.** ag RI cul ture
   - ◉ **B.** AG ri cul ture
   - ○ **C.** ag ri cul TURE
   - ○ **D.** ag ri CUL ture

4. They packed all of their <u>belongings</u> into the covered wagon.
   - ○ **F.** be long INGS
   - ○ **G.** BE long ings
   - ○ **H.** BE LONG ings
   - ◉ **J.** be LONG ings

5. A high <u>percentage</u> of people would not survive the cold winter.
   - ○ **A.** PER CENT age
   - ○ **B.** per cent AGE
   - ◉ **C.** per CENT age
   - ○ **D.** PER cent age

STOP

Name _____

Spelling Unstressed Syllables

Find the correctly spelled word to complete each sentence.
Fill in the circle beside your answer.

1. Mexican soldiers were seen riding in the _____.
   - ○ **A.** distunce
   - ○ **B.** distaince
   - ○ **C.** distence
   - ◉ **D.** distance

2. The mayor put up a _____ in the center of town.
   - ○ **F.** notis
   - ○ **G.** notise
   - ○ **H.** notic
   - ◉ **J.** notice

3. The mayor did not speak the same _____ as the soldiers.
   - ◉ **A.** language
   - ○ **B.** langwich
   - ○ **C.** languag
   - ○ **D.** langage

4. The soldiers' _____ tongue was Spanish, whereas we spoke English.
   - ○ **F.** nativ
   - ◉ **G.** native
   - ○ **H.** natieve
   - ○ **J.** natife

5. A _____ soldiers soon came riding into town.
   - ○ **A.** dozeen
   - ○ **B.** duzen
   - ◉ **C.** dozen
   - ○ **D.** dozin

Name _____

Vocabulary Dictionary: Suffixes

Read these dictionary entries and answer the questions that follow. Fill in the circle next to the best answer.

> **-less.** A suffix that forms adjectives meaning "without, free of."
>
> **-ly.** A suffix that forms adverbs and means "in a specified manner."

1. What is the meaning of the suffix in the underlined word?

   The stagecoach inched across the underline{swiftly} flowing river.

   ○ **A.** in a specified manner   ○ **C.** without, free of

   ○ **B.** characteristic of   ○ **D.** full of

2. What is the meaning of the suffix in the underlined word?

   The ranchers' underline{tireless} efforts saved the herd.

   ○ **F.** in a specified manner   ● **H.** without, free of

   ○ **G.** characteristic of   ○ **J.** full of

3. What is the meaning of the underlined word in the following sentence?

   The horse came back underline{riderless} to the barn.

   ○ **A.** with a rider   ○ **C.** with one more person than usual

   ● **B.** without a rider   ○ **D.** without someone leading the horse

4. What is the meaning of the underlined word in the following sentence?

   The small boy underline{carefully} weeded the vegetable garden.

   ○ **F.** free of care   ○ **H.** without care

   ○ **G.** without thought   ● **J.** tended with care

5. What is the meaning of the underlined word in the following sentence?

   Jamie was underline{powerless} to stop the runaway horse and carriage.

   ○ **A.** used power   ○ **C.** had no electricity

   ● **B.** without power   ○ **D.** was very strong

   (STOP)

Name _____

Grammar Possessive Pronouns

Find the correct possessive pronoun to replace the underlined word or words. Fill in the circle beside your answer.

1. "Who is coming to see <u>Luis's and my</u> play?" asked Jorge.
   - ○ **A.** mine
   - ○ **B.** their
   - ○ **C.** his
   - ◉ **D.** our

2. "Uncle Ned will come in <u>my mother's and sister's</u> wagon," said Carmen.
   - ◉ **F.** their
   - ○ **G.** them
   - ○ **H.** her
   - ○ **J.** its

3. "<u>The girl's</u> part will be played by Victoria," said Luis.
   - ◉ **A.** Her
   - ○ **B.** His
   - ○ **C.** Its
   - ○ **D.** Hers

4. "Sam, is this costume <u>Sam's</u>?" asked Carmen.
   - ○ **F.** his
   - ○ **G.** him
   - ◉ **H.** yours
   - ○ **J.** your

5. "<u>The costume's</u> collar is dirty and needs to be cleaned," said Jorge.
   - ○ **A.** His
   - ◉ **B.** Its
   - ○ **C.** My
   - ○ **D.** Mine

STOP

Name _____

Grammar Contractions

Find the correct contraction to replace the underlined words.
Fill in the circle beside your answer.

1. <u>I will</u> work in the field today.
   - ○ **A.** I'd
   - ◉ **B.** I'll
   - ○ **C.** I'm
   - ○ **D.** I've

2. <u>It is</u> going to be a warm day.
   - ○ **F.** Its
   - ○ **G.** It'll
   - ◉ **H.** It's
   - ○ **J.** It'd

3. <u>They have</u> planned to serve a meal at noon.
   - ○ **A.** They'll
   - ○ **B.** They'd
   - ○ **C.** They're
   - ◉ **D.** They've

4. <u>We are</u> going to wash our hands before we eat.
   - ○ **F.** We'll
   - ○ **G.** We've
   - ◉ **H.** We're
   - ○ **J.** We'd

5. <u>She has</u> baked an apple pie for us.
   - ◉ **A.** She's
   - ○ **B.** She'd
   - ○ **C.** She'll
   - ○ **D.** She're

STOP

Writing Skills Combining Sentences with Pronouns

Read the passage. Then read each question and fill in the circle next to the best answer.

Ma and Pa looked out over their land. They saw the new barn. They saw the crops growing in the fields.

A hen strutted across the yard and it clucked. It pecked at the ground, and it flapped its wings.

A colt kicked up its heels in the pasture. It ran to the fence. It neighed at the dog. It ate a carrot from Ma's hand.

Pa picked up an ax. He began chopping wood. He began whistling a tune as he worked.

Ma worked in the garden. She planted tomatoes. She planted corn.

1. What is the best way to combine the sentences in the first paragraph?

   ○ **A.** Ma and Pa looked out over their land. They saw the new barn and the crops growing in the fields.

   ○ **B.** After Ma and Pa looked out over their land, they saw the new barn. They saw crops growing in the fields.

   ○ **C.** Ma and Pa looked out over their land. They saw crops growing in the fields, and they saw the new barn.

   ○ **D.** Ma and Pa looked out over their land, and they saw crops and the new barn.

Go on

2. What is the best way to combine the sentences in the second paragraph?

○ **F.** A hen strutting across the yard clucked. It pecked at the ground. Then it flapped its wings.

○ **G.** A hen strutted across the yard and it clucked. It pecked at the ground, and it flapped its wings.

○ **H.** A hen strutted across the yard. It clucked, and it pecked at the ground. Then it flapped its wings.

◉ **J.** A hen strutted across the yard, clucked, pecked at the ground, and flapped its wings.

3. What is the best way to combine the sentences in the third paragraph?

○ **A.** A colt kicked up its heels, ran to the fence, it neighed at the dog, and ate a carrot.

○ **B.** A colt kicked up its heels in the pasture. It ran to the fence, and it neighed at the dog. Then it ate a carrot from Ma's hand.

◉ **C.** A colt kicked up its heels in the pasture, ran to the fence, neighed at the dog, and ate a carrot from Ma's hand.

○ **D.** A colt kicked up its heels in the pasture, and it ran to the fence. It neighed at the dog, and it ate a carrot from Ma's hand.

4. What is the best way to combine the sentences in the fourth paragraph?

◉ **F.** Pa picked up an ax and began chopping wood, whistling a tune as he worked.

○ **G.** Pa picked up an ax, he began chopping wood, and he began whistling a tune as he worked.

○ **H.** Pa picked up an ax. He began chopping wood, and began whistling a tune as he worked.

○ **J.** Pa picked up an ax. He began chopping wood. He began whistling a tune as he worked.

5. What is the best way to combine the sentences in the fifth paragraph?

- ○ **A.** Ma worked in the garden. She planted tomatoes, she planted corn.
- ◉ **B.** Ma worked in the garden, planting tomatoes and corn.
- ○ **C.** Ma worked in the garden, and she planted tomatoes and she planted corn.
- ○ **D.** Ma worked in the garden. She planted tomatoes, and she planted corn.

One Land, Many Trails

Level 5, Theme 5: Week 3

Weekly Skills Test Record

Student _____ Date _____

Student Record Form

	Possible Score	Criterion Score	Student Score
A: Making Judgments	5	4	
B: Syllabication VV, VCV, VCCV, and VCCCV Patterns	5	4	
C: Spelling Final /n/, Final /zhər/, Final /chər/, Final /ən/	5	4	
D: Vocabulary Dictionary: Parts of Speech	5	4	
E: Grammar Double Subjects	5	4	
F: Grammar Using *we/us* with Nouns	5	4	
TOTAL	30	24	
Total Student Score x 3.33 =			%

Name _____

Making Judgments

Read the journal entry. Then read each question and fill in the circle next to the best answer.

May 9, 1856

Journal Entry written by Clyde Snider

The school I go to is a small frame house with only one room. It has a blackboard and five rows of desks. During recess, we play in a nearby field or under the big oak tree in the schoolyard. I really enjoy walking to school every day.

My teacher's name is Miss Tucker. She's kind and patient, and I've learned a lot from her. In the winter, she arrives early to start a fire in the wood-burning stove. At noon, she cooks a meal for us while we play outside.

Miss Tucker brings books, maps, and supplies to school whenever she can find them. She makes difficult lessons easy to understand, and she gives us lots of practice exercises to help us learn. I enjoy all my subjects, although mathematics is sometimes hard for me.

The students range from first grade through eighth grade. Even though everyone has to study something different, Miss Tucker makes lessons for everyone. Sometimes the older students help the younger ones.

Unfortunately, I have a problem at school, and his name is Jamie Livermore. Jamie used to be a good friend of mine, and he's the best marble player in the county. Lately, though, he's been a bother. Whenever I need to work in class, he starts talking to me. He keeps talking until I turn around and ask him to be quiet. Then we both get into trouble. Yesterday, we had to stand in front of the class for fifteen minutes as punishment. Last week, we had to chop wood after school. I don't mind chopping wood, but I don't like being punished because Jamie doesn't follow the rules.

Tomorrow we're going to write a play about the explorers. Miss Tucker wants me to help two of the younger students. Tomorrow night, I'll write in my journal about what happens.

Go on ⇨

1. Which fact supports the judgment that Miss Tucker is a good teacher?
   - ○ **A.** She makes Jamie and Clyde chop wood.
   - ◉ **B.** She is good at explaining things.
   - ○ **C.** She builds fires in the winter.
   - ○ **D.** She is kind and patient.

2. Which fact supports the judgment that Clyde is a good student?
   - ○ **F.** He likes to walk to school.
   - ○ **G.** He likes his teacher.
   - ○ **H.** He and Jamie used to be good friends.
   - ◉ **J.** He helps out the younger students.

3. Which of these judgments could be based on the fact that Jamie talks in class?
   - ◉ **A.** Jamie gets his friend in trouble.
   - ○ **B.** Jamie is not a good student, especially in math.
   - ○ **C.** Jamie is one of the best marble players in the county.
   - ○ **D.** Jamie is a popular student.

4. From the information in the journal, what judgment can you make about Clyde's school?
   - ◉ **F.** The school was very different from today's schools.
   - ○ **G.** The students in Clyde's school learned more than today's students do.
   - ○ **H.** Miss Tucker was always well prepared.
   - ○ **J.** Going to school then was more fun than it is today.

5. From the information in the journal, which judgment can you make about one-room schoolteachers in the 1800s?
   - ○ **A.** The teachers had to like to walk.
   - ○ **B.** The teachers had an easy job.
   - ◉ **C.** The teachers had to work very hard.
   - ○ **D.** The teachers did not need to know much.

Syllabication VV, VCV, VCCV, and VCCCV Patterns

Choose the correct way to divide into syllables the underlined word in each sentence. Fill in the circle next to the best answer.

1. The cook <u>created</u> many dishes for the ranchers.
    ○ **A.** cr • eat • ed
    ○ **B.** crea • te • d
    ○ **C.** cr • ea • ted
    ◉ **D.** cre • at • ed

2. The ground was <u>solid</u> after years of dry weather.
    ○ **F.** so • lid
    ◉ **G.** sol • id
    ○ **H.** s • olid
    ○ **J.** soli • d

3. The hard <u>surface</u> made plowing difficult.
    ○ **A.** su • rface
    ◉ **B.** sur • face
    ○ **C.** surfa • ce
    ○ **D.** surf • ace

4. In an <u>instant</u> the clouds opened and rain fell.
    ○ **F.** ins • tant
    ○ **G.** inst • ant
    ○ **H.** insta • nt
    ◉ **J.** in • stant

5. The rancher held an <u>empty</u> bucket.
    ◉ **A.** emp • ty
    ○ **B.** empt • y
    ○ **C.** em • pty
    ○ **D.** e • mpty

Spelling Final /n/, Final /zhər/, Final /chər/, Final /ən/

Find the correctly spelled word to complete each sentence.
Fill in the circle beside your answer.

1. The soldiers on horseback were returning from an _____.
   - ○ **A.** advenchur
   - ○ **B.** advenzure
   - ○ **C.** advensur
   - ◉ **D.** adventure

2. The soldiers came riding down the _____ into town.
   - ○ **F.** mountin
   - ◉ **G.** mountain
   - ○ **H.** muontain
   - ○ **J.** mounten

3. Each one carried a _____ from his country.
   - ○ **A.** tresure
   - ◉ **B.** treasure
   - ○ **C.** treasur
   - ○ **D.** treazure

4. My mother pushed aside the _____ to watch them ride by.
   - ○ **F.** curtin
   - ○ **G.** curtan
   - ◉ **H.** curtain
   - ○ **J.** curtein

5. We polished the _____ in honor of the soldiers' arrival.
   - ○ **A.** furnitur
   - ○ **B.** furnitare
   - ○ **C.** furnichur
   - ◉ **D.** furniture

Vocabulary Dictionary: Parts of Speech

Read the following dictionary definition for the word *right*.
Then identify its part of speech in the sentences that follow.
Fill in the circle next to the best answer.

> **right** *n.* That which is morally proper or good. *-v.* To restore to an upright position. *-adj.* Located on the side opposite the left. *-adv.* In a correct manner, properly.

1. *Jeremy's desk is on the <u>right</u> side of his classroom.*
    - ○ **A.** noun
    - ● **C.** adjective
    - ○ **B.** verb
    - ○ **D.** adverb

2. *Good role models teach kids the difference between <u>right</u> and wrong.*
    - ● **F.** noun
    - ○ **H.** adjective
    - ○ **G.** verb
    - ○ **J.** adverb

3. *He taught me that it's faster to do a job <u>right</u> the first time.*
    - ○ **A.** noun
    - ○ **C.** adjective
    - ○ **B.** verb
    - ● **D.** adverb

4. *If you have a question, please raise your <u>right</u> hand.*
    - ○ **F.** noun
    - ● **H.** adjective
    - ○ **G.** verb
    - ○ **J.** adverb

5. *It took three of us to <u>right</u> the overturned boat.*
    - ○ **A.** noun
    - ○ **C.** adjective
    - ○ **B.** verb
    - ○ **D.** adverb

Grammar Double Subjects

Choose the sentence that is written correctly. Fill in the circle next to the best answer.

1. ○ **A.** Ben and I we will sing at the square dance tonight.
   ○ **B.** Harvey he sings with us sometimes.
   ◉ **C.** My mom and dad are going to attend.
   ○ **D.** My grandmother and grandfather they will also be there.

2. ○ **F.** Mom and my sister they made strawberry ice cream for refreshments.
   ◉ **G.** Aunt Sarah brought her tablecloth and a set of bowls.
   ○ **H.** Mom and Aunt Sarah they love to plan a party.
   ○ **J.** Tonight's dance it will be one to remember.

3. ○ **A.** Dad he can play the fiddle.
   ○ **B.** Dad and Uncle Owen they have played music all their lives.
   ○ **C.** My grandfather he taught them to play several different instruments.
   ◉ **D.** The music and dancing will start at six o'clock.

4. ◉ **F.** Maud will be the caller for the square dancing.
   ○ **G.** Maud and Elvin they know how to keep the dance lively.
   ○ **H.** Maud she taps her feet while she calls out the moves.
   ○ **J.** The band members and the dancers they love to hear Maud do the calling.

5. ○ **A.** Henry and Harry they will also be playing tonight.
   ○ **B.** Henry he might play his harmonica at the dance.
   ○ **C.** The harmonica and the fiddle they sound very good together.
   ◉ **D.** Many of the musicians say that Henry and Harry are the best.

Name _____

Grammar Using *we/us* with Nouns

Choose the sentence that is written correctly. Fill in the circle next to the best answer.

1. ○ **A.** All the people at the stable know we girls.
    ○ **B.** We girls can ride any horse we want.
    ○ **C.** Us girls know the best horses to ride.
    ○ **D.** It is us girls who train the horses each day.

2. ○ **F.** The rodeo is fun for us cowboys.
    ○ **G.** Us cowboys like to ride the bucking horses.
    ○ **H.** The clowns help to save we cowboys.
    ○ **J.** It is us cowboys who give thanks to the clowns.

3. ○ **A.** Us cowgirls can enter the barrel-racing contest at the rodeo.
    ○ **B.** A new girl must be well trained to race with we cowgirls.
    ○ **C.** We cowgirls have ridden in rodeos together for years.
    ○ **D.** The first ones to congratulate the winner are us cowgirls.

4. ○ **F.** Us rodeo fans must support our local rodeo events.
    ○ **G.** Us fans should attend every rodeo that we can.
    ○ **H.** The loudest cheers come from we longtime fans.
    ○ **J.** The cowboys and cowgirls appreciate us rodeo fans.

5. ○ **A.** Bull riding is the most dangerous event for us clowns.
    ○ **B.** Us clowns must keep the bulls away from the fallen cowboys.
    ○ **C.** Sometimes barrels are used to hide we clowns from the bulls.
    ○ **D.** Other times us clowns must outrun the bulls.

One Land, Many Trails

Level 5, Theme 5: Week 4

Weekly Skills Test Record

Student _____ Date _____

Student Record Form	Possible Score	Criterion Score	Student Score
A: Story Structure	5	4	
B: Changing Final *y* to *i*	5	4	
C: Spelling Changing Final *y* to *i*	5	4	
D: Vocabulary Dictionary: Word Histories	5	4	
E: Grammar Adverbs	5	4	
F: Grammar Comparing with Adverbs	5	4	
TOTAL	30	24	
Total Student Score x 3.33 =			%

Story Structure

Read the passage. Then read each question and fill in the circle next to the best answer.

The Trip to Town

Sally and her sister Amanda sat in the back of the wagon as it bumped along the road. "I can't wait to get to the general store," Sally said. "Ma said we could buy fabric to make new dresses. What color will you choose?"

Just as Amanda opened her mouth to answer, the wagon jerked to a stop. The horses tossed their heads, unable to pull the wagon any farther.

Pa climbed down and looked at the back left wheel. "It's stuck," he explained. "Everybody climb down and help me unload these sacks of grain. Unless we work quickly, we won't have time to go to the general store."

The family began lifting a dozen sacks of grain from the wagon. Pa needed to sell the grain at the market in town. While they worked, Sally hoped she didn't have to wait for next week's trip to get the fabric for her new dress.

When the wagon was finally empty, Pa helped Ma into the driver's seat. Ma picked up the reins. Then Pa slowly lifted the back of the wagon while Ma snapped the reins gently. The wagon lurched, then rolled easily forward. They reloaded the grain and soon they were on their way again.

At midmorning, they reached the edge of town. Sally saw people strolling along the wooden sidewalks. "Is there time to go to the general store, Pa?" she asked. Then she held her breath.

Pa reached into his pocket and pulled out a watch. He smiled as he answered, "I suppose we can spare a few minutes." Soon Sally was standing in front of racks of brightly colored fabrics. She immediately saw the green fabric she wanted. Before she knew it she was back in the wagon, rolling and bumping toward home.

1. Who is the main character in this story?
   - ○ **A.** Pa
   - ○ **B.** Ma
   - ○ **C.** Amanda
   - ◉ **D.** Sally

2. Where does most of the story take place?
   - ○ **F.** at the family home
   - ○ **G.** in the general store
   - ◉ **H.** on the road to town
   - ○ **J.** at the market

3. What is the problem in the story?
   - ○ **A.** Pa has to sell a dozen sacks of grain.
   - ◉ **B.** The wagon gets stuck.
   - ○ **C.** The horses toss their heads nervously.
   - ○ **D.** There is not enough fabric for two dresses.

4. What is one of the steps that helps to solve the problem?
   - ○ **F.** Pa takes a watch out of his pocket.
   - ○ **G.** Amanda opens her mouth to speak.
   - ○ **H.** Sally chooses a green fabric.
   - ◉ **J.** The family unloads the grain.

5. What is the most important reason that the family needs to get to town?
   - ◉ **A.** Pa needs to sell the sacks of grain.
   - ○ **B.** They need to get the wagon wheel fixed.
   - ○ **C.** The girls need to buy fabric.
   - ○ **D.** Pa needs to get a new watch.

Name _____

Changing Final *y* to *i*

Choose the correct base word for each underlined word below. Fill in the circle next to the best answer.

1. Ricardo <u>steadied</u> his horse as he rode toward the herd.
   - ○ **A.** steady
   - ○ **B.** steadi
   - ○ **C.** study
   - ○ **D.** stead

2. He <u>carried</u> a rope in his hand to rope the missing steer.
   - ○ **F.** carri
   - ○ **G.** careful
   - ○ **H.** care
   - ◐ **J.** carry

3. The cowboy was <u>hungrier</u> than he had been in days.
   - ○ **A.** hungriest
   - ○ **B.** hungri
   - ◐ **C.** hungry
   - ○ **D.** hungeriest

4. The calves this spring are <u>healthier</u> than those born last year.
   - ○ **F.** healthi
   - ◐ **G.** healthy
   - ○ **H.** healthiest
   - ○ **J.** healthful

5. The cowboy wrote two <u>stories</u> about this adventure.
   - ○ **A.** storie
   - ○ **B.** store
   - ○ **C.** stores
   - ◐ **D.** story

STOP

Spelling Changing Final *y* to *i*

Find the correctly spelled word to complete each sentence.
Fill in the circle beside your answer.

1. The settlers left many different _____ to move to the west.
    ○ **A.** citys   ○ **C.** cites
    ◉ **B.** cities   ○ **D.** cityes

2. Some said the _____ moment was when they first hit the trail.
    ◉ **F.** scariest   ○ **H.** scareyest
    ○ **G.** scaryest   ○ **J.** scariyest

3. Every member of the family had important _____ on the trip.
    ○ **A.** dueties   ◉ **C.** duties
    ○ **B.** dutys   ○ **D.** dutyes

4. Each day the landscape became _____ and more rugged.
    ○ **F.** lonleeyer   ◉ **H.** lonelier
    ○ **G.** lonlier   ○ **J.** lonelyer

5. At night, the settlers would stare at the _____ of the sky.
    ○ **A.** emptyness   ○ **C.** emptines
    ○ **B.** emtiness   ◉ **D.** emptiness

Name _____

Vocabulary Dictionary: Word Histories

Read the following dictionary definitions. Then answer the questions that follow. Fill in the circle next to the best answer.

---

café *n.* A coffee house or restaurant. [From French, coffee.]

inspire *v.* To create feeling or action. [From Latin *inspirare,* to breathe into.]

mathematical *adj.* Of or relating to mathematics. [From Greek *mathematikos,* from *mathema,* science, learning]

parade *n.* An organized public procession. [From Latin *parare,* to prepare.]

ragged *adj.* Dressed in tattered clothes. [From Middle English *ragge,* rag.]

---

1. On what word is the word *mathematical* based?

  ○ **A.** the Latin word *parare*   ○ **C.** the Greek word *parare*

  ◉ **B.** the Greek word *mathematikos* ○ **D.** the Latin word *mathematikos*

2. What is the meaning of *parare*?

  ○ **F.** science   ○ **H.** procession

  ○ **G.** learning   ◉ **J.** prepare

3. On what word is the word *ragged* based?

  ◉ **A.** on the Middle English   ○ **C.** on the Greek word
       word *ragge*   *mathematikos*

  ○ **B.** on the Latin word *inspirare* ○ **D.** on the Latin word *parare*

4. What is the meaning of *inspirare*?

  ◉ **F.** to breathe into   ○ **H.** coffee

  ○ **G.** rag   ○ **J.** science, learning

5. From what language did the word *café* originate?

  ○ **A.** Latin   ◉ **C.** French

  ○ **B.** Greek   ○ **D.** Middle English

STOP

Name _____

Grammar Adverbs

Choose the sentence that is written correctly. Fill in the circle next to the best answer.

1. ○ **A.** The girls rode swiftly through town.
    ○ **B.** One cowgirl whistled loud.
    ○ **C.** Final, they had found gold!
    ○ **D.** They sang songs and cheered happy.

2. ○ **F.** Jackson was riding his horse slow one afternoon.
    ○ **G.** Sudden the horse was frightened by a snake in its path.
    ○ **H.** The horse quick began galloping toward the rocks.
    ● **J.** Jackson calmly tugged on the reins to slow his horse.

3. ○ **A.** At night the wind blew gentle across the plain.
    ○ **B.** The stars sparkled bright in the huge sky.
    ● **C.** The sound of a harmonica drifted sadly from the camp.
    ○ **D.** The settlers sat weary around the fire.

4. ○ **F.** Alicia wanted bad to see a hawk.
    ● **G.** She had frequently heard how they soar in wide circles.
    ○ **H.** Sure a hawk would appear one day.
    ○ **J.** When she spotted a hawk, Alicia yelled loud.

5. ● **A.** The wagon train approached the river cautiously.
    ○ **B.** The settlers quick discussed where to cross the river.
    ○ **C.** They desperate hoped to cross it before dark.
    ○ **D.** At last they careful chose a spot where the water was low.

Name _____

Grammar Comparing with Adverbs

Choose the sentence that is written correctly. Fill in the circle next to the best answer.

1. ○ **A.** My horse needs to stop for water most frequenter than other horses.
   ○ **B.** My friend Jamie's horse stops most frequently than ours.
   ◐ **C.** Of all the horses in the wagon train, Mr. Dodd's horse stops most frequently.
   ○ **D.** Of the two horses we own, mine needs water most frequent.

2. ○ **F.** We planted our crops more late this season than last season.
   ○ **G.** Our crops were planted later of all those in the area.
   ○ **H.** Our neighbors usually plant their crops latest than we do.
   ◐ **J.** Of all our crops, corn is usually planted latest.

3. ◐ **A.** Walter finished his chores more quickly than his brother Ed.
   ○ **B.** In fact he was the quick of all his brothers.
   ○ **C.** Walter likes to work more quicker than his brothers.
   ○ **D.** Because Walter was the most quickest of all, he got to eat his supper first.

4. ○ **F.** Sue stitches a quilt carefulier than her younger sister.
   ◐ **G.** She sews the most carefully of all her brothers and sisters.
   ○ **H.** She sews carefuller every day.
   ○ **J.** Sue can sew carefully than her mother.

5. ○ **A.** Mary Lou wakes up earliest than her brother Clarence.
   ○ **B.** She often wakes up most early than her sister.
   ◐ **C.** Of all my friends, I wake up the earliest.
   ○ **D.** Do you wake up more earlier than your parents?

Animal Encounters

Level 5, Theme 6: Week 1

Weekly Skills Test Record

Student _____   Date _____

Student Record Form

	Possible Score	Criterion Score	Student Score
A: Making Generalizations	5	4	
B: Prefixes *com-*, *con-*, *en-*, *ex-*, *pre-*, *pro-*	5	4	
C: Spelling Prefixes *com-*, *con-*, *en-*, *ex-*, *pre-*, *pro-*	5	4	
D: Vocabulary Using Context	5	4	
E: Grammar Contractions with *not*	5	4	
F: Grammar Negatives	5	4	
G: Writing Skills Avoiding Double Negatives	5	4	
TOTAL	35	28	
Total Student Score x 2.86 =			%

Making Generalizations

Read the passage. Then read each question and fill in the circle next to the best answer.

Tonya's Kitten

Tonya's parents had promised her that she could get a dog or cat on her eleventh birthday. The day had come at last! She couldn't wait to go to the pet store in the mall. She knew that most pet owners love their pets, and she would, too.

Tonya's parents had told her that she would have to take care of the new pet by herself. She would give it water and food, and she would take care of it if it became ill.

Tonya's heart pounded in her chest as she walked into the pet store. She looked at the animals in their cages. The kittens were snuggled together, sound asleep. Like all puppies, the puppies were quite playful. Tonya didn't know which to choose, a puppy or a kitten.

Tonya asked the owner of the pet store for his advice. He said, "Owning a pet is always lots of fun. I think you should simply choose the animal that steals your heart."

Tonya walked past the cages again. A tiny brown puppy licked her hand. The puppy had soft fur and a pink tongue. Then Tonya walked over to the kittens. A black kitten awakened and stretched. The kitten looked at Tonya and meowed, as if to say, "Choose me!" It had the most beautiful green eyes Tonya had ever seen.

Tonya couldn't resist the kitten's plea. She picked it up and announced that the kitten would be her new pet. Then she asked the owner how to take care of it. He gave her several helpful hints and handed her a booklet called "Taking Care of Your Kitten."

When they got home, Tonya made a soft bed for her new kitten, Midnight. She held Midnight in her arms. "Cats make the best pets of all," she told her parents.

1. Which of the following sentences from the passage is an overgeneralization?
   - ○ **A.** She looked at the animals in their cages.
   - ○ **B.** Tonya asked the owner of the pet store for his advice.
   - ◉ **C.** Owning a pet is always lots of fun.
   - ○ **D.** Tonya walked past the cages again.

2. Based on the story, what generalization can you make about selecting a pet?
   - ◉ **F.** Selecting a pet can be very exciting.
   - ○ **G.** People usually select cats rather than dogs.
   - ○ **H.** Selecting a pet can take a very long time.
   - ○ **J.** People need help when selecting a pet.

3. Which word in the following sentence signals an overgeneralization?

   Like all puppies, the puppies were quite playful.
   - ○ **A.** like
   - ◉ **B.** all
   - ○ **C.** quite
   - ○ **D.** playful

4. Which of the following sentences from the story is a generalization?
   - ◉ **F.** Most pet owners love their pets.
   - ○ **G.** She couldn't wait to go to the pet shop at the mall.
   - ○ **H.** She would have to take care of the new pet by herself.
   - ○ **J.** The kittens were snuggled together, sound asleep.

5. Based on the story, what generalization can you make about taking care of a pet?
   - ○ **A.** Pets are very easy to care for.
   - ○ **B.** Pet owners always read books about their pets.
   - ○ **C.** Puppies are more playful than kittens.
   - ◉ **D.** Taking care of a pet is a big responsibility.

Name _____

Prefixes *com-, con-, en-, ex-, pre-, pro-*

Choose the correct meaning for the underlined word or words in each sentence. Fill in the circle next to the best answer.

1. The camp director asked the group to <u>conform</u> to the rules.
   - ○ **A.** follow
   - ○ **B.** write
   - ○ **C.** read about
   - ○ **D.** break

2. Larry feeds his goldfish food that is <u>enriched</u> with iron.
   - ○ **F.** made of
   - ◉ **G.** made richer
   - ○ **H.** lacking in
   - ○ **J.** bitter

3. Colin <u>exchanged</u> five old books for a new book on African animals.
   - ○ **A.** bought for very little money
   - ○ **B.** gave away for free
   - ○ **C.** sold for a price
   - ◉ **D.** traded for a substitute

4. The hikers took a first-aid kit as a <u>precaution</u>.
   - ○ **F.** guidepost
   - ○ **G.** sign of danger
   - ◉ **H.** care taken in advance
   - ○ **J.** trail

5. The hikers <u>proceeded</u> to the spot where the bear had last been seen.
   - ○ **A.** walked away from
   - ◉ **B.** moved toward
   - ○ **C.** ran quickly
   - ○ **D.** hiked in pairs

STOP

Name _____

Spelling Prefixes *com-*, *con-*, *en-*, *ex-*, *pre-*, *pro-*

Find the correctly spelled word to complete each sentence.
Fill in the circle beside the best answer.

1. My class took a field trip to a wildlife _____.
    - ○ **A.** preserv
    - ○ **C.** proserve
    - ○ **B.** perserve
    - ◐ **D.** preserve

2. The ranger expressed _____ about endangered animals living in the park.
    - ◐ **F.** concern
    - ○ **H.** comcern
    - ○ **G.** cuncern
    - ○ **J.** consern

3. She said that the park must _____ certain rules for visitors.
    - ○ **A.** enforse
    - ○ **C.** inforce
    - ○ **B.** inforse
    - ◐ **D.** enforce

4. She explained that the rules help maintain the good _____ of the park.
    - ◐ **F.** condition
    - ○ **H.** conditian
    - ○ **G.** condishun
    - ○ **J.** cundition

5. I hope we can _____ more ideas about wildlife next week.
    - ○ **A.** xchange
    - ○ **C.** exchang
    - ◐ **B.** exchange
    - ○ **D.** exchainge

Vocabulary Using Context

Choose the word or phrase that has the same meaning as the underlined word in each sentence. Fill in the circle next to the best answer.

1. The cheetah raced along at an amazing speed, easily <u>overtaking</u> the gazelle.
    ○ **A.** jumping higher than   ○ **C.** making friends with
    ○ **B.** falling behind   ◉ **D.** catching up with

2. Some male songbirds may <u>croon</u> a tune over 2000 times each day.
    ○ **F.** practice   ○ **H.** hear
    ◉ **G.** sing   ○ **J.** enjoy

3. A dog's hearing is so <u>acute</u> that it can hear sounds humans cannot.
    ○ **A.** attractive   ○ **C.** unaware
    ◉ **B.** sharp   ○ **D.** dull

4. The scientist carefully <u>excavated</u> the bones of the prehistoric creature from the hillside.
    ○ **F.** photographed   ◉ **H.** dug up
    ○ **G.** arranged   ○ **J.** fixed

5. Barn owls are mostly <u>nocturnal</u>, but occasionally they can be seen during the day.
    ◉ **A.** active at night   ○ **C.** dangerous
    ○ **B.** asleep at night   ○ **D.** protective of their young

Name _____

Grammar Contractions with *not*

Choose the sentence that is written correctly. Fill in the circle next to the best answer.

1. ○ **A.** We cant find the monkeys.
    ○ **B.** They have'nt been seen in several hours.
    ◐ **C.** They didn't come when we called.
    ○ **D.** We may'nt see them again.

2. ○ **F.** "Werent' you the one who wrote a paper on gorillas?" asked Gigi.
    ◐ **G.** "I didn't finish it," replied Alice.
    ○ **H.** "I wont be able to help you with it," Gigi said.
    ○ **J.** "Tha'ts all right," said Alice.

3. ◐ **A.** I wasn't able to see the baby giraffe.
    ○ **B.** The keeper didnt know when it was born.
    ○ **C.** I have'nt ever seen such a cute animal!
    ○ **D.** Wouldnt' you love to have a baby giraffe as a pet?

4. ○ **F.** The elephant doesnt look like a fierce animal.
    ○ **G.** Arent' elephants the largest animals in the wild?
    ◐ **H.** I don't think that elephants eat meat.
    ○ **J.** I could'nt eat leaves and roots the way an elephant does.

5. ○ **A.** Teresa had'nt seen a raccoon before.
    ◐ **B.** Wasn't she surprised when it ran up the tree?
    ○ **C.** The raccoon didnt notice Teresa.
    ○ **D.** It hasnt' found any scraps of food.

Name _____

Grammar Negatives

Choose the sentence that is written correctly. Fill in the circle next to the best answer.

1. ○ **A.** They have no more food for the zebras at the zoo.
   ○ **B.** I haven't ever seen no zebras at the zoo.
   ○ **C.** The zebras have not never been so friendly.
   ○ **D.** The giraffes can't not see them over the fence.

2. ○ **F.** The elephant can't reach no leaves.
   ○ **G.** It won't need nothing for a while.
   ○ **H.** Hasn't anyone brought food for the elephant?
   ○ **J.** Jodie wouldn't get too close to no elephant.

3. ○ **A.** Michiko hasn't never been to the Reptile House.
   ○ **B.** She wasn't ready to see any snakes.
   ○ **C.** She won't go no further.
   ○ **D.** Michiko isn't coming to the zoo no more.

4. ○ **F.** I didn't take no pictures of the cheetah.
   ○ **G.** My camera does not have no film in it.
   ○ **H.** I won't never have another chance like this.
   ○ **J.** Don't you have any film you could give me?

5. ○ **A.** The zoo never had polar bears until this year.
   ○ **B.** There wasn't never no water for them around here before.
   ○ **C.** Hasn't no one else seen the two new polar bears?
   ○ **D.** I hadn't seen neither polar bear.

Name _____

Writing Skills Avoiding Double Negatives

Read the sentences below. Fill in the circle next to the sentence that is written correctly.

1. ○ **A.** The lion did not catch no prey today.
   ○ **B.** It never saw no other animals at all.
   ◉ **C.** The giraffes did not find very much food either.
   ○ **D.** They could never stretch their long necks high enough to get no leaves.

2. ○ **F.** Ana could not find no eggs in the chicken house.
   ◉ **G.** She looked under the bench but saw nothing there.
   ○ **H.** Jack didn't find no peaches in the peach trees.
   ○ **J.** He will not never plant that kind of tree again.

3. ◉ **A.** The gazelles do not have any shade.
   ○ **B.** They can't find no trees for shelter.
   ○ **C.** The baby gazelle doesn't never leave its mother's side.
   ○ **D.** I never saw nothing so cute.

4. ○ **F.** Sarah hasn't never seen a python.
   ○ **G.** Jaime didn't have no pictures of one.
   ◉ **H.** Mary could not recall if she had any pictures.
   ○ **J.** Aren't there none of them in that book?

5. ○ **A.** The dolphins would not eat none of the fish.
   ○ **B.** I never saw a dolphin turn down no food.
   ○ **C.** The nearest aquarium has not never had dolphins.
   ◉ **D.** None of the dolphins I've seen have been in the wild.

Animal Encounters

Level 5, Theme 6:, Week 2

Weekly Skills Test Record

Student _____ Date _____

Student Record Form	Possible Score	Criterion Score	Student Score
A: Topic, Main Idea, and Supporting Details	5	4	
B: Three-Syllable Words	5	4	
C: Spelling Three-Syllable Words	5	4	
D: Vocabulary Dictionary: Pronunciations	5	4	
E: Grammar Prepositions	5	4	
F: Grammar Prepositional Phrases	5	4	
G: Writing Skills Combining Sentences with Prepositional Phrases	5	4	
TOTAL	35	28	
Total Student Score x 2.86 =			%

Topic, Main Idea, and Supporting Details

Read the passage. Then read each question and fill in the circle next to the best answer.

Please Don't Feed the Animals

Have you ever fed pieces of bread to a duck? Perhaps you have left picnic scraps for a squirrel. Even though it's fun to feed wild animals, it's almost always a bad idea. One reason for this is that the animals may become dependent on the food that people provide. The animals may also teach their young to beg for food. This may cause the animals to go too close to dangerous cars and homes. It's best if they stay in their natural habitats.

It's also dangerous for people to be around wild animals. Wild animals are interested in getting something to eat, not in making friends. If an animal learns that a certain person will give it food, the animal may chase that person. Geese often chase people with food. Squirrels have climbed up people's legs, scratching them. If a person receives such an injury from an animal, the person might become ill.

Another reason not to feed wild animals is that food that is good for people may not be healthy for animals. An animal's natural diet is well balanced for the animal. The food that people eat often contains more sugar, salt, and fat than animals need to be healthy. Some food may even kill an animal.

Feeding wild animals can also be expensive. The park rangers at national parks will charge a fine to a person who feeds wild animals. People who run the national forests want to keep the wildlife healthy. As a result, the fines may be as high as $500.00.

1. What is the topic of this passage?
   - ○ **A.** squirrels and geese
   - ○ **B.** diets of wild animals
   - ◉ **C.** feeding wild animals
   - ○ **D.** park rangers

2. Which sentence states the main idea of the passage?
   - ○ **F.** Some food that people eat can kill an animal.
   - ◉ **G.** People should not feed wild animals.
   - ○ **H.** Animals may chase people with food.
   - ○ **J.** It's best if animals stay in their natural habitats.

3. Which detail supports the idea that it's dangerous to be around wild animals?
   - ○ **A.** Animals may teach their young to beg for food.
   - ○ **B.** A person can be charged $500.00 for feeding a wild animal.
   - ○ **C.** An animal's natural diet is well balanced for the animal.
   - ◉ **D.** A person who is injured by an animal could become ill.

4. Which sentence from the third paragraph states the paragraph's main idea?
   - ◉ **F.** Another reason not to feed wild animals is that food that's good for people may not be healthy for animals.
   - ○ **G.** An animal's natural diet is well balanced for the animal.
   - ○ **H.** The food that people eat often contains more sugar, salt, and fat than animals need to be healthy.
   - ○ **J.** Some food may even kill an animal.

5. Which detail supports the main idea that feeding wild animals can be expensive?
   - ○ **A.** Animals may become dependent on the food that people feed them.
   - ○ **B.** Squirrels sometimes run up people's legs.
   - ○ **C.** Animals dependent on food from humans may come too close to cars.
   - ◉ **D.** Fines for feeding wild animals may be as high as $500.00.

STOP

Three-Syllable Words

For each item, fill in the circle next to the word that is divided into syllables correctly.

1. *disagree*
   - ○ **A.** di • sag • ree
   - ◐ **C.** dis • a • gree
   - ○ **B.** dis • ag • ree
   - ○ **D.** di • sa • gree

2. *thankfully*
   - ○ **F.** than • kful • ly
   - ○ **H.** thank • full • y
   - ◐ **G.** thank • ful • ly
   - ○ **J.** tha • nkf • ully

3. *acceptance*
   - ◐ **A.** ac • cep • tance
   - ○ **C.** a • ccept • ance
   - ○ **B.** ac • cept • ance
   - ○ **D.** acc • ep • tance

4. *conference*
   - ◐ **F.** con • fer • ence
   - ○ **H.** confe • re • nce
   - ○ **G.** conf • er • ence
   - ○ **J.** con • fere • nce

5. *generous*
   - ○ **A.** ge • ner • ous
   - ○ **C.** ge • nero • us
   - ○ **B.** gene • r • ous
   - ◐ **D.** gen • er • ous

Name _____

Spelling Three-Syllable Words

Find the correctly spelled word to complete each sentence.
Fill in the circle beside your answer.

1. The nature park that we visited is very _____.
   - ○ **A.** popyular
   - ○ **B.** populur
   - ○ **C.** popalar
   - ◉ **D.** popular

2. It was a beautiful day to walk in a _____ setting.
   - ○ **F.** naturl
   - ○ **G.** natiral
   - ◉ **H.** natural
   - ○ **J.** naturale

3. A guide drew our _____ to the dry, cracked ground.
   - ◉ **A.** attention
   - ○ **B.** attintion
   - ○ **C.** attanntion
   - ○ **D.** attenshun

4. He said that the lack of rain had created a _____ setting for the animals.
   - ○ **F.** dangrous
   - ◉ **G.** dangerous
   - ○ **H.** dangerus
   - ○ **J.** danjerous

5. He told us they would _____ to bring in water for the animals.
   - ○ **A.** contenue
   - ○ **B.** continyoo
   - ◉ **C.** continue
   - ○ **D.** kentinue

Vocabulary Dictionary: Pronunciations

Look at the following dictionary entries and use them to answer the questions. Fill in the circle next to the best answer.

---

falcon (făl′kən) or (fôl-) or (fô′kən) *n.* Any of several long-winged, swift-flying hawks.
rodeo (rō dē ō) or (rə dā′ō) *n.* A public performance of people riding and roping livestock.
tomato (tə mā′tō) or (tə mä′tō) *n.* A round, yellow or red fruit, used as a vegetable.

---

1. How many different pronunciations are there for the word *falcon*?
   - ○ **A.** one
   - ○ **B.** two
   - ◉ **C.** three
   - ○ **D.** four

2. What two ways could you pronounce the vowel sound in the first syllable of the word *falcon*?
   - ○ **F.** like the vowel sounds in *pay* and *pat*
   - ◉ **G.** like the vowel sounds in *pat* and *paw*
   - ○ **H.** like the vowel sounds in *pay* and *pot*
   - ○ **J.** like the vowel sounds in *paw* and *toe*

3. What two ways could you pronounce the vowel sound in the second syllable of the word *rodeo*?
   - ○ **A.** like the vowel sounds in *pay* and *pot*
   - ○ **B.** like the vowel sounds in *tin* and *pay*
   - ◉ **C.** like the vowel sounds in *tea* and *pay*
   - ○ **D.** like the vowel sounds in *end* and *tea*

Go on ⇨

4. How many different pronunciations are there for the word *tomato*?

○ **F.** one

◉ **G.** two

○ **H.** three

○ **J.** four

5. What two ways could you pronounce the vowel sound in the second syllable of the word *tomato*?

◉ **A.** like the vowel sounds in *play* and *father*

○ **B.** like the vowel sounds in *add* and *end*

○ **C.** like the vowel sounds in *care* and *ace*

○ **D.** like the vowel sounds in *plot* and *care*

Grammar Prepositions

Read the sentences below. Find the preposition in each sentence. Fill in the circle next to the best answer.

1. Charles took the injured calf to the veterinarian.

   ○ **A.** took   ● **C.** to

   ○ **B.** the   ○ **D.** veterinarian

2. The man looked at the calf and sighed.

   ○ **F.** looked   ○ **H.** calf

   ● **G.** at   ○ **J.** sighed

3. The calf had a deep cut above its hoof.

   ○ **A.** calf   ○ **C.** deep

   ○ **B.** had   ● **D.** above

4. The veterinarian calmly searched inside the cupboard.

   ○ **F.** searched   ○ **H.** calmly

   ● **G.** inside   ○ **J.** cupboard

5. In a few seconds, he had found the antiseptic.

   ● **A.** In   ○ **C.** found

   ○ **B.** few   ○ **D.** seconds

STOP

Name _____

Grammar Prepositional Phrases

Read the sentences below. Find the prepositional phrase in each sentence. Fill in the circle next to the best answer.

1. The calf put its head on the man's chest and blinked its eyes.
   - ● **A.** on the man's chest
   - ○ **B.** The calf
   - ○ **C.** put its head
   - ○ **D.** and blinked its eyes

2. The man gently rubbed some medicine on the calf's leg.
   - ○ **F.** The man
   - ○ **G.** gently rubbed
   - ○ **H.** some medicine
   - ● **J.** on the calf's leg

3. A woman with a blue scarf helped the man bandage the leg.
   - ○ **A.** A woman with
   - ● **B.** with a blue scarf
   - ○ **C.** helped the man
   - ○ **D.** bandage the leg

4. Charles helped the man slip a blanket beneath the calf.
   - ○ **F.** helped the man
   - ○ **G.** slide a blanket
   - ○ **H.** a blanket beneath
   - ● **J.** beneath the calf

5. Five minutes later, the calf walked back to its pen.
   - ○ **A.** Five minutes later
   - ○ **B.** the calf walked
   - ○ **C.** walked back
   - ● **D.** to its pen

Writing Skills Combining Sentences with Prepositional Phrases

Choose the best way to combine each pair of sentences by using a prepositional phrase. Fill in the circle next to the best answer.

1. Please get the puppy's leash. It is in the closet.

   ○ **A.** Please get the puppy's leash, because it is in the closet.
   ◉ **B.** Please get the puppy's leash from the closet.
   ○ **C.** Please get the puppy's leash which is in the closet.
   ○ **D.** Please get the puppy's leash; it is in the closet.

2. We saw a mother giraffe. She was with her baby.

   ◉ **F.** We saw a mother giraffe with her baby.
   ○ **G.** We saw a mother giraffe, and she was with her baby.
   ○ **H.** We saw a mother giraffe, and we saw her baby.
   ○ **J.** We saw a mother giraffe; she was with her baby.

3. The elephant is a large animal. It has huge floppy ears.

   ○ **A.** The elephant is a large animal, and it has huge floppy ears.
   ○ **B.** The elephant is a large animal; it has huge floppy ears.
   ○ **C.** The elephant is a large animal since it has huge floppy ears.
   ◉ **D.** The elephant is a large animal with huge floppy ears.

4. The big cats are asleep. They sleep near a rock cave.

- ○ **F.** The big cats are asleep, which is near a rock cave.
- ◉ **G.** The big cats are asleep near a rock cave.
- ○ **H.** The big cats are asleep, for they sleep near a rock cave.
- ○ **J.** The big cats are asleep with a rock cave.

5. Our group left the zoo. It was closing time.

- ○ **A.** Our group left the zoo it was closing time.
- ○ **B.** Our group left the zoo and it was closing time.
- ◉ **C.** Our group left the zoo at closing time.
- ○ **D.** Our group left the zoo; it was closing time.

Animal Encounters

Level 5, Theme 6: Week 3

Weekly Skills Test Record

Student _____ Date _____

Student Record Form	Possible Score	Criterion Score	Student Score
A: Drawing Conclusions	5	4	
B: Information and Study Skills Completing Application Forms	5	4	
C: Suffixes -*ent*, -*ant*, -*able*, -*ible*	5	4	
D: Spelling Suffixes -*ent*, -*ant*, -*able*, -*ible*	5	4	
E: Vocabulary Dictionary: Run-On Entries	5	4	
F: Grammar Object Pronouns in Prepositional Phrases	5	4	
G: Grammar Pronouns as Compound Objects of Prepositions	5	4	
TOTAL	35	28	
Total Student Score x 2.86 =			%

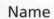
Drawing Conclusions

Read the passage. Then read each question and fill in the circle next to the best answer.

Erika's Gift

Erika tore the paper off her gift. "Just what I wanted!" she exclaimed. She held up a new camera and a roll of film.

Erika had decided that she wanted to become a wildlife photographer some day. She had spent hours looking at images of animals in magazines like *National Geographic*. She had read books about photography and cameras. Now she had her own camera! "A good place to start would be right in my own back yard," she thought.

Erika's house sat on the top of a hill. Her back yard sloped down to a clump of oak trees and a small pond. Her family often spotted raccoons, squirrels, birds, and even deer from the kitchen window. Erika liked to take walks in the yard just so she could be outside.

Erika carefully read the instruction booklet that came with the camera. Then she loaded the film. At last, she was ready to take some pictures! She went outside and walked toward the pond. Along the way, she took a picture of a blue jay. The blue jay flew away just as she snapped the shutter. This didn't discourage her, though, because she had read that photographers must take many pictures to get one good shot.

At that moment, Erika saw a deer walk to the pond. The deer didn't see her because she was several yards away. It looked cautiously around and then lowered its head. As it began drinking, Erika quietly adjusted the zoom lens on her camera. She knew that she could get a close-up shot of the deer even from this distance.

Erika aimed the camera at the deer and began clicking. When she had shot five pictures, she stopped. She wanted to have time to watch this beautiful animal before it wandered away. She smiled as she looked at the deer. She knew she had taken at least one fabulous shot.

1. Why does Erika feel that her own back yard is the best place to start taking pictures?

   - ○ **A.** It is pretty.
   - ○ **B.** She won't have to leave home.
   - ○ **C.** It is safe.
   - ◉ **D.** Her family sees animals there.

2. Which of the following details supports the conclusion that Erika knows a lot about photography?

   - ○ **F.** She receives a camera and a roll of film as a gift.
   - ◉ **G.** She reads many books and knows how to work the equipment.
   - ○ **H.** She often spots wild animals from her kitchen window.
   - ○ **J.** She takes a picture of a blue jay and several pictures of a deer.

3. Why does Erika know how to use a zoom lens?

   - ◉ **A.** She read the instruction booklet.
   - ○ **B.** She learned how to use it from her father.
   - ○ **C.** She saw a show about it on television.
   - ○ **D.** She learned about zoom lenses at school.

4. Which of these conclusions can you draw about Erika from reading the story?

   - ○ **F.** She likes to roll down the hill in her yard.
   - ◉ **G.** She likes being outdoors.
   - ○ **H.** She often watches television shows about animals.
   - ○ **J.** She is very close to her parents.

5. Why does Erika take five pictures of the deer?

   - ○ **A.** She doesn't know how to work the camera.
   - ○ **B.** The camera takes the pictures automatically.
   - ◉ **C.** She wants to be sure to get one good shot.
   - ○ **D.** She wants to have five good shots of the deer.

Information and Study Skills
Completing Application Forms

Read the application. Then answer the questions that follow. Fill in the circle next to the best answer.

Stephanie has signed up to help at the animal shelter in her town. Before she starts her job, she wants to learn as much as possible about animals. She goes to the library and picks up this application for a library card.

BOOKWORM LIBRARY CARD

To apply for a Bookworm Library Card, you must be under 16 years of age. Complete this form and turn it in to the main library or any branch. Bring an adult who has a photo I.D. and proof of address.

NAME

1. First Name _____   2. Last Name _____

3. First and Last Name of Parent or Guardian _____

ADDRESS

4. Street _____   5. Apartment No. ____

6. City _____   7. State _____   8. ZIP Code _____

PHONE NUMBER

9. Area Code/Phone Number _____

10. Phone Number of Parent or Guardian _____

IDENTIFICATION

11. Date of Birth Mo. Day. Yr. _____

12. Name of School _____

13. School's Phone Number _____

I understand that I should take good care of all library materials checked out in my name and that I should return them on time.

14. Signature _____

I assume responsibility for all materials checked out and all charges for materials that are turned in late. I understand that library fees are set by the city council and may change. I agree to inform the library if the card is lost or stolen.

15. Signature of Parent or Guardian _____

Go on ⟹

---

1. What will Stephanie write on line 8?
    - ○ **A.** the name of her street
    - ◉ **B.** her ZIP code
    - ○ **C.** the name of her school
    - ○ **D.** her area code

2. What should Stephanie do if she doesn't know the phone number of her school?
    - ○ **F.** She should leave the line blank.
    - ○ **G.** She should call the school and ask.
    - ◉ **H.** She should look up the number in the phone book.
    - ○ **J.** She should write her home phone number.

3. Who should sign the form?
    - ○ **A.** only Stephanie
    - ○ **B.** Stephanie and the librarian
    - ◉ **C.** Stephanie and her parent or guardian
    - ○ **D.** only Stephanie's parent or guardian

4. What should Stephanie do with her completed application?
    - ○ **F.** use it to take out books at the library
    - ○ **G.** give it to her teacher
    - ○ **H.** turn it in at a city council meeting
    - ◉ **J.** take it to the main library or a branch library

5. What should Stephanie do **right after** she completes the application?
    - ◉ **A.** read it over to check for mistakes
    - ○ **B.** drop it in the mail
    - ○ **C.** take it to the library with a parent or guardian
    - ○ **D.** check out some books

Name _____

Suffixes *-ent, -ant, -able, -ible*

Choose the correct meaning for each underlined word. Fill in the circle next to the best answer.

1. Mrs. Smith was a new <u>resident</u> at my apartment building.
   - ○ **A.** window washer
   - ○ **B.** manager
   - ◉ **C.** neighbor
   - ○ **D.** gardener

2. The zookeeper is an <u>immigrant</u> from China.
   - ◉ **F.** someone who moves to a place
   - ○ **G.** a person who works with animals
   - ○ **H.** an important person
   - ○ **J.** someone who likes animals

3. The fragile glass swans were quite <u>breakable</u>.
   - ○ **A.** very sturdy
   - ◉ **B.** easily broken
   - ○ **C.** attractive
   - ○ **D.** very small

4. My mother says that Smoky Bear hats and mugs are <u>collectibles</u>.
   - ○ **F.** books for collectors
   - ○ **G.** shelves to hold a collection
   - ○ **H.** a collector's displays
   - ◉ **J.** things that can be collected

5. The cowboy reported that the cattle herd was <u>manageable</u>.
   - ○ **A.** tired and hungry
   - ○ **B.** able to run very fast
   - ○ **C.** loud and rough
   - ◉ **D.** able to be controlled

STOP

Name _____

Spelling Suffixes *-ent, -ant, -able, -ible*

Find the correctly spelled word to complete each sentence. Fill in the circle beside the best answer.

1. My teacher said that because it had not rained, it was _____ that some wild animals would starve.
   - ● **A.** possible
   - ○ **B.** possibel
   - ○ **C.** posbile
   - ○ **D.** possable

2. He told us that several species of animals were already _____ from the woods.
   - ○ **F.** absant
   - ○ **G.** abbsent
   - ● **H.** absent
   - ○ **J.** abssent

3. At the park headquarters, we saw a _____ display.
   - ○ **A.** remarkible
   - ● **B.** remarkable
   - ○ **C.** remakable
   - ○ **D.** remarckable

4. The guide said that animals must be _____ if there are sudden weather changes.
   - ○ **F.** adaptible
   - ● **G.** adaptable
   - ○ **H.** adeptable
   - ○ **J.** adaptabul

5. We learned that wild animals that are _____ on only one type of food have a harder time surviving.
   - ● **A.** reliant
   - ○ **B.** reliunt
   - ○ **C.** relient
   - ○ **D.** ralient

Name _____

Vocabulary Dictionary: Run-On Entries

Answer the following questions. Fill in the circle next to the best answer.

1. Under which word would you look in a dictionary to find the meaning of the word *tenderness*?

   ○ **A.** tend   ◉ **C.** tender
   ○ **B.** tending   ○ **D.** tenderly

2. Under which word would you look in a dictionary to find the meaning of the word *joyous*?

   ◉ **F.** joy   ○ **H.** joyfully
   ○ **G.** joyful   ○ **J.** joyless

3. Under which word would you look in a dictionary to find the meaning of the word *chatterer*?

   ○ **A.** chattering   ○ **C.** chatters
   ◉ **B.** chatter   ○ **D.** chattered

4. Under which word would you look in a dictionary to find the meaning of the word *collectible*?

   ○ **F.** collection   ○ **H.** collecting
   ○ **G.** collected   ◉ **J.** collect

5. Under which word would you look in a dictionary to find the meaning of the word *payable*?

   ○ **A.** paid   ◉ **C.** pay
   ○ **B.** paying   ○ **D.** payment

Grammar Object Pronouns in Prepositional Phrases

Choose the sentence that is written correctly. Fill in the circle next to the best answer.

1. ○ **A.** The pet store sent a letter to she.
   ○ **B.** My father read the letter to I.
   ○ **C.** The letter said that they would give we a gift.
   ● **D.** The gift will be delivered to her.

2. ○ **F.** My mother took a photograph of I with the cat.
   ○ **G.** The children gathered around she to look at it.
   ○ **H.** My mother told they that the cat is named Little.
   ● **J.** She gave the picture to me after the picnic.

3. ● **A.** My uncles gave the fishing pole to me after my birthday dinner.
   ○ **B.** Their grandfather gave it to they many years ago.
   ○ **C.** My brother wanted me to put the pole in front of he.
   ○ **D.** My sister asked if her could fish with the pole soon.

4. ○ **F.** Antonia came over to show her drawings to we.
   ○ **G.** Antonia's dog Sam was with she.
   ● **H.** Sam jumped up on us and licked our faces.
   ○ **J.** Antonia had to grab hold of he.

5. ○ **A.** Sheryl sent the package to I by regular mail.
   ○ **B.** I received the package from she today.
   ● **C.** John asked if I would show the gift to him.
   ○ **D.** John thought that Sheryl's gift for I was wonderful.

Name _____

Grammar Pronouns as Compound Objects of Prepositions

Choose the sentence that is written correctly. Fill in the circle next to the best answer.

1. ◯ **A.** Max threw the ball to Taylor and he.
   ◯ **B.** Then Taylor threw it to Ellen and I.
   ◯ **C.** My dog brought the ball to Ernie and her.
   ◯ **D.** We laughed at Mabel and she.

2. ◯ **F.** Ellen bought the movie tickets for Max and me.
   ◯ **G.** We sat in back of she and her sister.
   ◯ **H.** Between you and I, I was confused by the ending.
   ◯ **J.** Next time I go with Max and they, I'll choose the movie.

3. ◯ **A.** Carla put the puzzle on the table between Harry and me.
   ◯ **B.** It was a challenge for he and I to find the edge pieces.
   ◯ **C.** We wanted to finish without help from my sisters or she.
   ◯ **D.** When the puzzle was done, everyone cheered except they and Carla.

4. ◯ **F.** Mr. Rodriguez sang the new song to Margaret and she.
   ◯ **G.** "Did you write that song for Ellen and I?" asked Margaret.
   ◯ **H.** "No, a friend wrote it for me and my parents," he said.
   ◯ **J.** "She performed it for me and they last Saturday."

5. ◯ **A.** Weijan wrote the story with Mary and she.
   ◯ **B.** We enjoyed the story about the mascot and him.
   ◯ **C.** Next week he will read it for Harry and I.
   ◯ **D.** Mary will copy the words for Weijan and they.